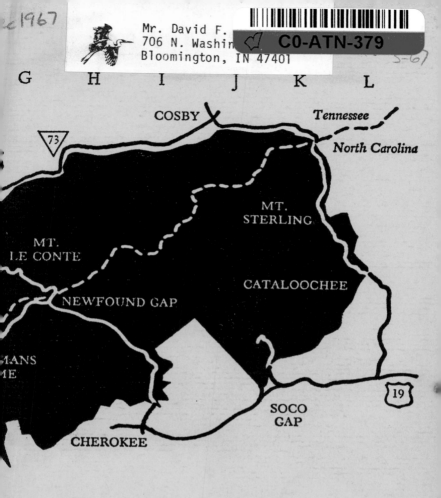

IN THE GREAT SMOKY MOUNTAINS

MUSHROOMS of the great smokies

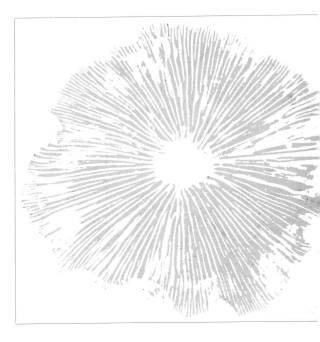

The University of Tennessee Press, Knoxville

MUSHROOMS

OF THE GREAT SMOKIES

a field guide to some mushrooms and their relatives

L. R. HESLER

TO ARTHUR STUPKA

naturalist   *scholar*   *friend of science*

Preface

This book is addressed to the inquiring amateur. It presents some representatives of the mushrooms and their relatives of the fertile region, the Great Smoky Mountains National Park. Although the book describes those species of mushrooms that occur within the Park, it should be understood that many of these species are also Southern Appalachian and even world-wide in their occurrence. On the other hand a few are known only from the Great Smokies or from within the Park itself. The inclusion of these mountains within the National Park guarantees within its borders a permanent succession of mushroom crops for all favorable seasons to come.

For a better understanding, a definition of the words mushroom and mushroom relatives should be established. The term mushroom is used here for any fleshy, gill-bearing fungus. Some mushrooms are edible, and others are poisonous. If one chooses to use the term toadstool to refer to a poisonous mushroom, he may do so. A difficulty here, however, is that some persons employ the term toadstool to designate all wild mushrooms. Mushroom relatives are those conspicuous fungi which bear a natural relationship to the mushrooms.

The area, the Great Smoky Mountains National Park, extends along the state-line ridge between Tennessee and North Carolina. The boundary on the northeast is near the Pigeon River in the vicinity of

Cosby, Tennessee; the southwestern border is the Little Tennessee River near Calderwood, Tennessee, and Tapoco, North Carolina. The Park is rich in mushrooms and other fungus inhabitants which, except in mid-winter, may be observed along the trails. Those who wish to collect mushrooms and other fungi in the Park must first obtain a permit from the Superintendent.

In this volume, Part One deals briefly with some of the natural aspects of mushrooms; Part Two describes some representatives of the mushrooms of the Park; Part Three has to do with mushroom relatives. Some of the species treated are rare; others are common; and still others have only recently been described and are relatively new to science.

Acknowledgment

This book is the product of cooperative effort. Each of the Park Superintendents in turn has, through liberal policy, made the field work possible. Park Naturalist Arthur Stupka, through his enthusiasm for and understanding of flora studies, has been a constant stimulus in my work. This perhaps is adequate excuse to dedicate the book to Mr. Stupka, but my principal reason was to recognize the contributions that he has made to the National Park Service, the Great Smoky Mountains National Park, The University of Tennessee, and to the discipline of Natural History.

The manuscript itself has undergone a series of drafts. An early copy was read critically by Mr. Stupka; Dr. A. J. Sharp, Professor of Botany, The University of Tennessee; Dr. Alexander H. Smith, the foremost American mushroom authority, The University of Michigan; Mr. Carlos C. Campbell, an informed Park enthusiast, of Knoxville; Professor A. R. Shields, Roanoke College; and Mrs. Esther C. Hesler. Although most of their suggestions have been followed, the author assumes responsibility for both style and content. When typing the manuscript Miss Marjorie Silvers made valuable suggestions directed toward clarity. Mrs. Romance F. Carrier prepared the line drawings of the Park and of a generalized mushroom. To all of these persons I acknowledge my obligations for their thoughtful contributions. Finally, a substantial portion of the publication cost of this volume has been borne by the L. R. Hesler Research Fund which was recently established by alumni, friends of science, and members of The University of Tennessee Faculty. To each of these who brought this Fund into being I humbly extend my grateful appreciation.

The University of Tennessee,   L. R. HESLER
Knoxville,
May, 1960.

Contents

PART THREE: MUSHROOM RELATIVES

Key to Common Larger Fungi, page 185

PART ONE
MUSHROOMS IN NATURE

The Park
as a Mushroom Garden

One of the arresting features of the Great Smoky Mountains National Park is its variety and abundance of mushrooms. Their development is encouraged by the luxuriant tree population and by the generous annual rainfall. In an average year, the rainfall may range from 50 inches at lower elevations to 85 inches on the high mountains.

Within the Park, the cone-bearing trees often form stands of considerable extent; especially is this true of spruce and fir at the higher elevations. Pines and hemlocks are found at intermediate and lower elevations. As for the deciduous trees, the Park is one of the very rich areas in the temperate zone.

In addition to forests and rainfall, there are other factors and conditions which contribute indirectly to a great many kinds of mushrooms. Tree variety and density are affected by direction and degree of slope, and these in turn involve exposure, temperature, and drainage. Rock formations vary from limestone and graywacke to schists—each having its influence on trees, humus, and other elements of mushroom environment. Range in altitude, from 1400 to 6600 feet, affects temperature and rainfall. Temperature decreases and rainfall increases with altitude. These factors do not, of course, act separately, but interact in a complexity difficult to describe. The complex and varied environment of the Park accounts for the development of a diverse mushroom population.

The forest trees, dropping their leaves or needles, build a carpet of humus. Disintegration of their trunks, limbs, stumps, and roots also contributes to this humus accumulation. Here, in the Park, rain-soaked humus and soil produce a highly favorable substratum for the development of an exciting mushroom population.

In the Park, not only are mushrooms numerous, but also growing there are hundreds of mushroom relatives, including slime molds, downy mildews, powdery mildews, cup fungi, dead-man's-fingers, morels, earthtongues, rusts, jelly fungi, bracket fungi, spine-bearing fungi, boletes, coral fungi, puffballs, earthstars, bird's-nest fungi, stinkhorns, and false truffles. True truffles have been found once, and it is probable that they may be a rarity in the Park.

Fungus Populations of the Park

Although a trip into the Park at any season will reveal members of the fungus family, their favored seasons are summer and autumn. After adequate rains, from May to December, mushrooms and other larger fungi may appear in impressive numbers. One can hardly record individual populations—assuredly these are at times amazingly great—but the number of kinds of all fungi collected to date is about two thousand. To name a few, an unpublished list of Park fungi includes: thirty earthtongues, five true morels, ninety-nine cup fungi (fairy-baths), eighty-four rusts, thirty-eight coral fungi, forty-one toothed fungi (hydnums), one hundred and forty-eight polypores, eighty-three boletes, forty members of the puffball and earthstar tribes, and nine hundred mushrooms. One can only guess as to how many more fungi will be added to the Park list, but the number of mushrooms alone might eventually total fifteen hundred.

The Park mushroom flora is interesting, not only because of the numbers of individuals and species, but also because of the kinds which grow there. Some are world-wide in occurrence; others are known only in North America; and several are new to science. When the Park was officially established in 1934, a permanent, natural mushroom garden was guaranteed.

The Parts
of a Mushroom

The story of the mushroom itself needs brief narration. At this point, that story may well begin in the woods. At almost any time, the leaf mold, if overturned, will reveal white, stringlike strands extending near the surface through the humus-layer. These strands, called *rhizomorphs*, are composed of many interwoven, slender filaments—*hyphae*, collectively called *mycelium*.

As the mycelium grows through the humus, it absorbs food, some of which is stored in that mycelium. With suitable temperatures and adequate rains, knoblike developments appear on the strands—the young mushrooms, popularly called "buttons." With sufficient moisture these buttons, within a few hours, develop into mature mushrooms. Thus, all mushrooms, in the course of their development, exhibit a button stage.

The typical full-grown mushroom, or *fruiting body*, is composed of a *stalk* which, in most instances, extends upright and bears an umbrella-shaped *cap*. In turn, the cap bears, on its lower surface, radiating, vertically-arranged plates—the *lamellae*, or *gills*. On the faces of these gills the reproductive cells, called *spores*, develop in fabulous numbers—millions on one fruiting body. At maturity, the spores are ejected free of the gill and float slowly to the ground. In still air, they fall directly to the humus below, and in mass reveal the color characteristic of the species. Spores in mass, as seen in a spore deposit, may be white, cream, yellow, clay, brown, pink, lilac, purplish, or black, or various

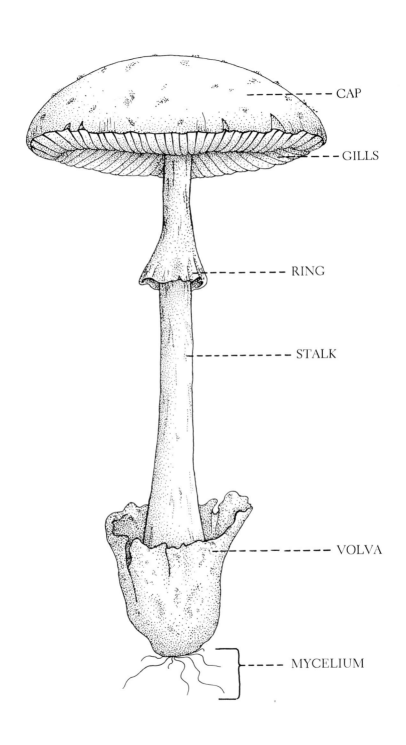

CAP

GILLS

RING

STALK

VOLVA

MYCELIUM

shades and tints, depending on the species. A spore deposit, if desired, may be prepared as follows: detach a mature cap from its stalk, place it gill-side down on white paper, and cover with an inverted tumbler or dish for five to ten hours. If mature, the spores will fall and accumulate on the paper in a pattern which matches that of the gills, and from which the color of the deposit can be readily viewed. If a spore deposit is not available, spore color may usually be inferred from the gill color.

Some of the normally discharged spores ultimately fall on a favorable substratum, where they germinate (sprout) to form new hyphae and finally a mycelium. When these hyphae develop ropelike strands (rhizomorphs), the buttons may begin to form.

If the young mushroom is cut longitudinally through the stalk and cap, there is revealed, in some mushrooms but not all, a webby or membranous curtain called the *inner veil*, which connects the edge of the cap with the stalk. As the cap expands, this curtain breaks, according to the species, in one of three ways: (1) the veil-remnants may remain around the stalk as a *ring*, or *annulus*; (2) the veil may break clean of the stalk but remain, for a short time, as a hanging fringe on the cap-margin; (3) the veil may be so sparse or rudimentary as to leave no trace of itself. In many mushrooms, the veil is entirely absent.

In some mushrooms, such as species of *Amanita*, another important structure, the *outer*, or *universal*, *veil*, is observed when the young mushroom is cut vertically through the cap and stalk. In the young stage, this veil envelops the whole button. As the cap expands and the stalk elongates, this enveloping veil breaks in different ways, according to the species. Further details are given under the Amanitas on page 24.

Anyone who would attempt to identify mushrooms needs to keep in mind that developmental variations of the fruiting body may occur. Of importance in identifying mushrooms are color, surface characters, odor, and taste of the cap; the mode of attachment of the gills, their width, spacing, and color in both the young and mature stages; the character and developmental behavior of the inner and universal veils, if present; the color of the spores in mass; the habit, manner of growth, and the substratum of the mushroom (soil, humus, decaying wood, dung).

In addition to these characters one must, with a good microscope, determine the size, shape, and surface characters of the spores, and the minute, structural details of the gills. Without these and other microscopic features, few but the better known mushrooms can be identified.

The mushroom hunter may prepare his own spore deposit, such as the one here from Entoloma strictius, slightly enlarged.

Edible and Poisonous Mushrooms

The Europeans have used wild mushrooms as food since Greek and Roman times. Many Americans, on the contrary, fearing the probability of being poisoned, show a definite distrust of them. But there are always persons who are interested in the general subject of edible and poisonous mushrooms. It is with this group in mind that the following comments on edible and poisonous mushrooms are made.

For each species described in this book, it is indicated whether the species is edible or poisonous. In most instances, the designation as to edibility is based on the reports of other writers rather than on personal experience. As a matter of fact, I have eaten only a few wild species of fungi, including the common meadow mushroom (*Agaricus campestris*), the glistening *Coprinus* (*C. micaceus*), the orange-brown *Lactarius* (*L. volemus*), the common morel (*Morchella esculenta*), and the sulphur polypore (*Polyporus sulphureus*). It is a good policy to use extreme caution in eating wild mushrooms, and it is recommended that ONE EAT ONLY THOSE MUSHROOMS KNOWN TO HIM TO BE EDIBLE.

There are many popular rules for distinguishing edible and poisonous species. So far as is known, not one of these rules is safe. The general recommendations are that you should eat only those species you know to be safe; and you should avoid all species which are not known to you to be positively edible. This means that you should begin by learning to recognize species and to learn their names. This learning project is no more difficult than learning to know accurately a few birds or wild flowers and their names. Once you learn to recognize an edible species, such as *Agaricus campestris* (the common meadow mushroom), you can be sure of its edibility. You may wonder how it becomes known, in the first instance, whether a given species is edible or poisonous. The method for determining edibility is by eating. A long list of species have thus been tested and recorded. Once you have correctly identified a mushroom, reference to available books may state whether or not the species is edible. If a person wishes to test an unknown mushroom, he should begin with a small bit, then a larger and larger piece at intervals of a few days. One making such tests must understand the risk involved. A poisonous mushroom can have serious or even fatal effects.

To become informed about poisonous mushrooms, one should begin by getting acquainted with the Amanitas. Although a few *Amanita* species are edible, it is within this group that the most poisonous of the mushrooms are found. Their characteristics and habits are discussed and illustrated on pages 24–40.

Among the most potently poisonous Amanitas is A. *brunnescens* (Figure 1f). This has been erroneously called *Amanita phalloides*, but it is doubtful whether the latter species occurs in the eastern United States. Symptoms of poisoning from A. *brunnescens* begin to appear in the patient within six to fifteen hours after eating it. Then sudden abdominal pains, vomiting, cold sweat, diarrhea, and thirst appear in the patient. The nervous system is gradually paralyzed, and within four to ten days collapse and death follow. Children may die within four to six days, adults within eight to ten days; but, if a large quantity is eaten, death may occur within two days. The active principle seems to be amanita-toxin. Since it resists heat, *Amanita brunnescens*, if eaten, even when it has been cooked, may still be deadly!

There is no satisfactory treatment for poisoning by *Amanita brunnescens*. By the time the patient becomes ill, it is usually too late to ward off trouble. A physician should, of course, be called at once. Emetics and purgatives should be administered. Writers do not agree on the question of whether an effective serum is available. Atropin, rather effective against poisoning by

Amanita muscaria (the fly mushroom), is of no value for poisoning by A. *brunnescens.*

Another death-dealing mushroom is the destroying angel, *Amanita verna* (Figure 1a). It seems to be just as lethal as A. *brunnescens.* It is pure white and a very beautiful, innocent-looking fungus with poisonous properties like those of A. *brunnescens.*

Still another member of this group is *Amanita muscaria,* the fly mushroom (Figure 1l). It is found in the Park along road banks in sandy or gravelly soil between Newfound Gap and Smokemont. When eaten, it induces symptoms that are distinctive and quite different from those caused by A. *brunnescens* and A. *verna.* The symptoms appear within one to two hours (at times five to six hours), depending on the quantity eaten. In the patient, the toxic substance, called muscarin, induces excessive salivation and perspiration, nausea, flow of tears, vomiting, diarrhea, slow pulse, and accelerated respiration. In addition, mental symptoms appear in the form of giddiness, confusion of ideas, and at times hallucinations. Fortunately, atropin is an antidote for the toxic principle of the fly mushroom.

The green-gilled *Lepiota* (*L. molybdites,* Figure 3a), a large, handsome mushroom, when eaten causes illness. Its poison seems less lethal than that of the Amanitas. Nevertheless, it can cause serious sickness, and one death is on record. Heating largely destroys its toxic properties. This species is often confused with the parasol mushroom (*Lepiota procera,* Figure 3d) which is edible. Its gills do not turn greenish at maturity as they do in *L. molybdites.* The toxic principle causes vomiting, diarrhea, difficulty of swallowing, and burning pains in the stomach.

The jack-o'-lantern (*Clitocybe illudens,* Figure 9a) has a reputation of causing illness. Of the recorded cases of poisoning, none is reported to be fatal. Boiling seems to destroy the toxic principle which is muscarin-like in its properties and behavior.

There are other species of poisonous mushrooms, but the foregoing discussion should suffice to convince one that any poisonous species should not be eaten. The consequences may, indeed, be grave. Some more mildly poisonous kinds are eaten, sometimes with appropriate ceremony, with a subsequent stimulating effect by the toxic substance. Here the reader is referred to the section on hallucinogenic mushrooms.

Hallucinogenic Mushrooms

There is a group of mushrooms which in mild doses is slightly poisonous, and which induces a mild intoxication in man. One of these, *Amanita muscaria* (Figure 11), is deliberately eaten by certain peoples of Asia and elsewhere. It causes giddiness, and a kind of hallucination.

Relatively recent researches have brought to light that for several centuries references have been made to a sacred fungus employed as a narcotic by the Indians of Mexico. The Aztecs and others called the fungus "teonanacatl," which now seems to be a term for any hallucinogenic mushrooms used by them. Recent studies by the mycologist, Dr. Rolf Singer, indicate that several species of *Psilocybe* are hallucinogenic and are used in certain ceremonies in the Huautla region of Mexico. His list follows: *Ps. aztecorum, Ps. caerulescens, Ps. cubensis, Ps. mexicana, Ps. muliercula,* and possibly *Ps. candidipes.*

These species are used by the Mexican Indians in ceremonial rites which are usually secretly carried out. *Life* magazine (May 13, 1957) reported that R. Gordon Wasson, a New York banker, and others were able to attend one of these ceremonies. At this rite, they partook of the vision-giving mushrooms. A strict ritual was observed with a "curandera," or practitioner, acting as mistress of ceremonies. The mushrooms were cleaned, passed through burning incense and, accompanied by prayers before an altar, were apportioned in pairs to those attending. Darkness in the room then followed. Within a half hour the visions came, accompanied at the beginning by nausea. The nausea disappeared, and artistic objects of bright colors appeared. Later visions of palace gardens, all covered with semi-precious stones, came into view. Visions of unreality of many sorts came to the white participants among the twenty other Indian adults—all observing a ceremony, religious in character and carried out with decorum. Chanting in the native language accompanied the rite. It is a ceremony that goes back many generations and seems to play an important part in the lives of certain Indian tribes of Mexico.

Fairy Rings

Mushroom collectors have long observed in both meadow and forest that many species grow either in circles or arcs of circles. When a spore sprouts, the resulting mycelium spreads radially through the humus or the grass roots. If there are no obstacles, and if food is uniformly available, a circular mat of mycelium develops. In time, the mycelium at its central point of origin dies, and there remains then a ring of mycelium. Finally the mushrooms develop at equally distant points from the center of the mat, and thus form a circle of mushrooms; this is the fairy ring. Such rings are more often found in pastures or on lawns. In the forest, mycelial growth is often interrupted by tree roots, logs, stumps, or rocks, so that arcs are more common than circles.

A close examination of a fairy ring on grassy soil reveals other interesting features. As the mushroom mycelium advances, it causes changes in the soil, an important one being the production of nitrogen-salts.

These compounds, fertilizing the soil, stimulate the grass to form a dark-green ring. Within this dark-green circle, the mycelium produces changes which cause the grass to die, and there appears a bare, circular zone.

The phenomenon of fairy rings has been recorded for centuries. Before the nature of mushroom growth was understood, fairy rings were attributed to fairies, witches, goblins, and spirits; to snails and slugs; and to lightning.

Mycorrhiza:
Fungus-Root Association

One will not collect mushrooms long before he will note that certain species grow under certain trees. For more than a century, it has been known that the mycelium of some mushrooms associates with tree roots. The small, absorbing roots of many trees show a mycelial sheath—an association called *mycorrhiza* (fungus-root).

At favorable intervals, mycorrhizal species produce fruiting bodies. Within limits, there is specialization in mycorrhizal association. More than one kind of mushroom may form mycorrhiza with a given tree species; and a mushroom species may form mycorrhizal relationships with more than one tree species. Among the more common mycorrhizal mushrooms and their relatives are certain species of *Amanita, Cortinarius, Lactarius, Russula, Tricholoma,* and *Boletus.*

The benefits to the associates in a mycorrhizal relationship are assumed to be that the absorption of certain elements from the soil by the tree is facilitated; in turn, the mushroom probably derives some benefit from its association with tree roots, but the exact story is still steeped in debate.

Parasitic Mushrooms

The vast majority of mushrooms, existing as scavengers, live on the decaying humus of the forest. Many species live in association with the roots of trees, as already described. Another interesting mode of life is that in which one mushroom lives as a parasite on another kind of mushroom. In the Park, two species, *Asterophora lycoperdoides* and *Asterophora parasitica*, have been found parasitizing species of *Russula* and *Lactarius*.

Similar types of parasitism are found also among the mushroom relatives. One which has been collected is *Boletus parasiticus* (Figure 33a). It grows in the Park as a parasite on *Scleroderma aurantium*, a puffball.

Another group of fungi, belonging to the genus *Cordyceps*, is parasitic on various kinds of insects and on false truffles (*Elaphomyces*). Further remarks on this group will be found on page 241.

Autodigestion

The inky cap mushrooms, members of the genus *Coprinus*, are familiar to students of nature. In some of them, but not all, the gills at maturity become a liquid mass blackened by the spores. This phenomenon is a physiological process, characteristic of *Coprinus comatus* (shaggy mane, Figure 29a), *Coprinus micaceus* (glistening *Coprinus*, Figure 29b), and others of the group. The process, although commonly called deliquescence, is autodigestion.

In *Coprinus comatus*, toward maturity, the edge of the cap and gills move outward radially away from the stalk, and the gills become separated from one another. The spores are ripened and discharged progressively from the edge of the gill upward. The gill then secretes a digestive enzyme which dissolves it from the edge upward. In this manner, the spore-freed portion of the gill is cleared from the path of the other maturing spores above.

This process of autodigestion begins with the flesh of the gill. The solid part is converted into a liquid by the action of a digestive enzyme secreted by the gill. The process requires about twenty-four hours to digest the gills of a small fruiting body of *C. comatus* and about two days for the gills of a large fruiting body.

Not all species of *Coprinus* exhibit this autodigestive process. In *C. plicatilis*, common on lawns, the gills simply dry up without any deliquescence.

The black liquid has been used as ink. One author (Ramsbottom) states that an Australian suggestion is for police to carry "pistols" containing Indian ink impregnated with spores of different species. A stain on clothing, made during a mêleé, would be recognized as one "fired" by a policeman's particular pistol.

Luminescence

Among the strange phenomena displayed by both animals and plants is the production of light without heat. This observable fact has been the subject of speculation and inquiry for a long period of time, attracting the attention of both Aristotle and Pliny.

Everyone is familiar with the firefly and its light, and those who have tramped in the woods at night may have encountered "fox fire"—the light of luminous wood. These are but two of many examples of luminescence among organisms.

Within the Park, luminescence is displayed by certain species of mushrooms and, perhaps, by some of the relatives of mushrooms. The luminous mushrooms include at least three rather common species:

the honey agaric (*Armillaria mellea*, Figure 2a); the jack-o'-lantern (*Clitocybe illudens*, Figure 9a); and the small, astringent *Panus* (*P. stypticus*, Figure 18a). These and certain other species of mushrooms, as well as a few relatives, give off a soft light observable in darkness. In some species, it is the cap which is luminous; in others, only the gills are luminous; in still others, only the mycelium; and, finally, in one Asiatic mushroom (*Mycena rorida* variety *lamprospora*), the spores are brilliantly luminescent. The luminous quality is generally found only in fresh specimens or in the younger, active parts.

The honey agaric (Figure 2a), in its usual cycle, develops mycelium which grows in strands, or rhizomorphs. These strands pervade the wood and bring about decay. While the strands are young and fresh, they give off a luminous glow. Thus, it is the fungus strands in the wood, rather than the wood itself, which is luminous. The cap, gills, and stalk of this mushroom, on the contrary, do not glow. The light given off is sometimes called "fox fire" by the natives, woodsmen, and foresters. In some instances the light is rather strong. It is said that people of the Far North may mark their trails with bits of decaying wood invaded by a luminous fungus.

In the jack-o'-lantern, the gills of fresh specimens yield a soft light visible only in darkness. Neither the cap nor stalk nor the old gills are luminous.

In America, *Panus stypticus* is luminous—especially its gills, but also to some extent its cap and mycelium. Interestingly enough the European form of this mushroom is nonluminous. The American and European forms otherwise seem to be the same species.

Other mushrooms which have some luminous capabilities include certain species of *Pleurotus* in the Eastern Hemisphere, especially *P. japonicus*, *P. lampas*, *P. lunaillustris*, and perhaps others.

Within the genus *Mycena*, luminous species include *M. flavida*, *M. tintinnabulum*, *M. polygramma*,

M. *illuminans,* and several other species from the islands of southeastern Asia.

Luminescence is reportedly found in a few species of mushroom relatives. Two species of dead-man's-fingers (*Xylaria polymorpha,* Figure 43a, and X. *hypoxylon,* Figure 43b) are said to be luminous. It is claimed that *Fomes annosus* and *Polyporus sulphureus* (Figure 32a) are luminescent, but the light attributed to them may be traceable to the accompanying honey agaric (*Armillaria mellea*). The poroid mushroom, *Dictyopanus luminescens,* is a luminous species from Malaya.

The color of the light produced varies somewhat with the species of mushroom. It may be greenish-white in *Panus stypticus;* white in *Pleurotus japonicus;* or it may range from yellowish through green into blue in the honey agaric. The light, whatever its color, is continuous through both day and night. The chain of causal factors which might explain the phenomenon of luminescence is still the subject of inquiry.

PART TWO
MUSHROOMS IN THE PARK

Key to
Common Mushroom Genera

There are two choices on the left, each with the same number, 1–1, 2–2, etc. If the first choice applies to the specimen to be identified, follow the dotted line to the right of the number. If that number is 2, then proceed downward on the left to the pair of 2's, and make a choice there. This procedure should be followed until the genus name is reached.

The italic number preceding the name of each genus refers to the order of appearance of that genus in this book—i.e., Amanita is first (1); Armillaria is second (2); etc. Within each genus, the species are given an "a," "b," "c," etc., designation.

1. Spore-mass white, or in some species creamy-yellow to buff; rarely lilac or greenish 2
1. Spore-mass not as above 18
   2. Fruiting body fleshy, not tough 3
   2. Fruiting body tough 16
3. Ring or volva or both present on the stalk 4
3. Ring and volva both absent 6
   4. Volva present, if not as a cup then as scaly remnants on the cap or stalk-base .. *1, Amanita*
   4. Volva absent; ring present 5
5. Gills attached to the stalk ....*2, Armillaria*
5. Gills free, not attached to the stalk ...*3, Lepiota*
   6. Stalk lateral or excentric ....*4, Pleurotus*
   6. Stalk central 7
7. Gills waxy ....*5, Hygrophorus*
.........................*6, Laccaria*
7. Gills not waxy 8
   8. The mushroom parasitic on another mushroom species; gills often poorly developed
.......................*7, Asterophora*
   8. The mushroom not parasitic 9

23. Spore-mass yellow-brown or rusty-brown 24
23. Spore-mass purple-brown or black 26
    24. Gills easily separating from the cap . . . .
    . . . . .24, *Paxillus*
    24. Gills not as above .25
25. Stalk central; inner veil cobweb-like, conspicuous
    . . . . .25, *Cortinarius*
25. Stalk lateral or absent; inner veil none or indis-
    tinct [not illustrated] . . . .*Crepidotus*
    26. Spore-mass purple-brown 27
    26. Spore-mass black .29
27. Ring absent; veil-remnants at first hanging to cap-
    margin . . . . .26, *Naematoloma*
27. Ring present 28
    28. Gills free, not attached to the stalk . . . .
    . . . . .27, *Agaricus*
    28. Gills attached to the stalk . . . .28, *Stropharia*
29. Gills dissolving, or deliquescing, at maturity . . . .
    . . . . .29, *Coprinus*
29. Gills not deliquescing . . . . . .30, *Pseudocoprinus*

1

Amanita

Among the mushrooms in the Great Smokies, few, if any, have achieved the notoriety of the Amanitas. They have long been widely talked about because some of them are poisonous.

Following the rains of summer and early autumn, they are conspicuous and at times abundant in the woods of Cades Cove and similar areas, and a few are found in the spruce-fir forests of the high elevations.

Some species of *Amanita* are white; others, according to the species, are either gray, smoky, brown, yellow, orange, or red. Cap color is rather constant for the species.

The spores, in mass, are white or cream. The gills are only slightly attached to the stalk, or more often do not reach it. But the more distinctive characteristics, found on the stalk, are an inner veil and an outer (universal) veil.

In many young Amanitas, although not all, a webby or membranous inner veil extends from the cap-margin to the stalk. As the cap expands, the inner veil breaks and may either remain attached to a point near the top of the stalk, where it forms the annulus, or ring; or, it may remain partly or wholly attached to the cap-margin. In some Amanitas, there is no inner veil and therefore no ring.

The outer, or universal, veil completely envelops the young *Amanita*. As the stalk elongates, this veil breaks, according to the species, in one of three ways: (1) when the outer veil breaks at the top, it remains at the stalk-base as a membranous cup, called the volva; (2) when it breaks toward the middle, it leaves the lower portion adhering variously to the (often bulbous) base; (3) finally, it may leave only warty, mealy, or scaly fragments around the stalk-base. In many Amanitas, the outer veil leaves scaly fragments on the cap-surface.

Often when an *Amanita* is pulled from the soil the volva or other veil-remnants at the base are left behind. If this happens, a critical character of the *Amanita* is lost to the collector, and the mushroom cannot then be identified. In any event, since our most poisonous mushrooms belong to the genus *Amanita*, the collector is strongly urged to avoid eating any *Amanita*!

There are now known in the Smokies some thirty different Amanitas, twelve of which are included in the key.

Key to Amanita Species

1. Cap white or whitish 2
1. Cap colored, at least on the center 4
  2. Cap scaly, base of stalk bulbous...............3
  2. Cap smooth, without scales .... .1*a*, *verna*
3. Cap and flesh with an odor of chloride of lime or old ham; stalk somewhat mealy but not scaly; the inner veil fragile and soon disappearing....1*b*, *chlorinosma*
3. Cap and flesh without special odor; stalk with circles of recurved scales at the base; the inner veil persisting, often attached to the stalk by fibers ......1*d*, *solitaria*
  4. The outer veil leaving a white volva or cup at the stalk-base 5
  4. Outer veil not leaving a cup at the stalk-base ...6
5. A ring, or annulus, present on the upper portion of the stalk; cap red or orange ....1*g*, *caesarea*
5. No ring present at any time on the stalk; cap brownish, tan, buff, or orange ....1*c*, *fulva*

6. A ring, or annulus, absent; the outer veil leaving fragile particles at the stalk-base, no volva cup; cap red, fading to yellow ....*1e, parcivolvata*

6. A ring present on the stalk 7

7. Cap brownish, smoky, or olive-buff; the outer veil leaving a narrow rim or line on the bulbous stalk-base ....*1f, brunnescens*

7. Cap otherwise colored 8

8. Cap reddish-brown; the cap, flesh, and stalk becoming reddish where bruised, with pallid scales which become reddish ....*1h, rubescens*

8. Cap, flesh, and stalk not becoming reddish where bruised 9

9. Cap pallid or pale yellow, usually tinged slightly greenish, with soft, flat scales which are often tinged wine-color; odor of radish ....*1i, mappa*

9. Cap not as above; odor mild 10

10. Outer veil forming a membranous volva which adheres to the stalk-base; cap yellow; ring disappearing early in development .....*1j, gemmata*

10. Outer veil not membranous but leaving particles on the stalk-base; cap yellow, orange, or red ...11

11. Cap 1 to 2½ inches broad, yellow; ring yellow, membranous, persistent ....*1k, flavoconia*

11. Cap 3 to 5 inches broad, yellow, orange, or red; ring whitish, fringed, scarcely membranous, often disappearing ....*1l, muscaria*

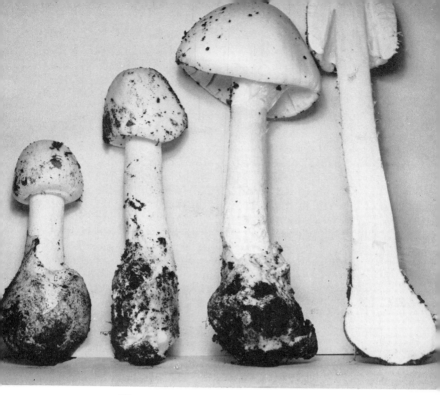

Figure 1a, about one-half natural size

1a   *Amanita verna*

DESTROYING ANGEL   DEADLY POISONOUS

Cap 2½ to 5 inches broad, white, viscid, without scales. Odor mild to slightly nauseous. Gills white, crowded. Stalk 4 to 7 inches or more in length, white, bulbous. Ring white, ample. Volva membranous, cuplike, finally appressed to the bulb. Spores white in mass.

In deciduous and mixed woods, at times under pines, more common at elevations below 3000 feet. It has been collected at several points in the Park, in both North Carolina and Tennessee, from June to October.

The destroying angel is deadly poisonous! Its frequency and abundance after summer rains, and being pure white throughout, strongly tempt the mushroom hunter. One is reminded that this is the most deadly of all mushrooms known.

1b   *Amanita chlorinosma*

This is one of the largest and most conspicuous mushrooms in the Park.

Mushroom students give conflicting reports on its edibility. Some say it is edible; others class it as dangerously poisonous. It should certainly not be eaten.

Cap 3 to 12 inches broad, whitish or tinged pale cream, with soft warty scales on the central portion, soft powdery fragments outward. Odor usually strong of chloride of lime, or occasionally resembling that of old ham. Gills white to cream-color, close. Stalk 4 to 12 inches long, enlarged at the ground line, often rooting, the surface mealy. Ring fragile and soon disappearing. Volva remains appear as a mealy powder at the base of the stalk and on the pileus. Spores white in mass.

On soil, in deciduous and coniferous woods, July to November. When summer and early autumn rains come, it is conspicuous in Cades Cove, near Cosby, and elsewhere at lower elevations.

Figure 1b, about two-thirds natural size

1c *Amanita fulva*

TAWNY AMANITA   EDIBLE

Cap 1 to 3½ inches broad, color fulvous, but varying from shades of tawny to orange or buff, with one or two white patchlike scales which soon disappear, margin conspicuously striate. Odor mild. Gills white, close, narrow. Stalk 3 to 6 inches or more in length, whitish above, fulvous below. Ring none. Volva ample, white, membranous, deep cuplike. Spores white in mass.

The tawny *Amanita* is said to be of mediocre quality, without much distinct flavor when cooked. It occurs generally over the world, from Greenland to Alabama, west to Oregon and California, and in Europe and Asia.

It is found throughout the Park, in deciduous, coniferous, and mixed woods, at both high and low elevations. *Amanita livida*, a gray to livid species, and the white *Amanita alba* resemble *Amanita fulva*; these also occur in the Park. From June to August, one may expect the tawny *Amanita* in Cades Cove, on Mt. Le Conte, at Alum Cave Parking Area, Indian Gap and Indian Creek, and on Clingmans Dome.

Figure 1c, about three-fourths natural size

Figures 1d, above, detail of veil natural size;
right, mushrooms two-thirds natural size

1d   *Amanita solitaria*

SOLITARY AMANITA   EDIBILITY DOUBTFUL

Cap 3 to 6 inches broad, white, at times ivory-yellow, with conspicuous, pyramidal warts. Odor mild. Gills ivory to buff, close. Stalk 4 to 11 inches long, enlarged at ground line, and rooting below the bulb, with concentric, recurved scales on the bulb. Ring large, white, at first adhering to the gills, lower portion at one stage of development attached to the stalk by strong fibers. Volva remnant as scales on both the bulb and pileus. Spores white or pale cream in mass.

On soil, in deciduous and mixed woods, at times in pine woods, from Abrams Creek (near Chilhowee) on the western side of the Park to Greenbrier on the east, at both high and low elevations, June through August.

This *Amanita* and *Amanita chlorinosma* are two of the largest, most conspicuous whitish mushrooms in the Smokies. Handsome as it is, the solitary *Amanita* should not be eaten.

Figure 1e, about two-thirds natural size

1e *Amanita parcivolvata*

SLIGHT-VOLVATE AMANITA   POISONOUS

This *Amanita* is distinguished from *Amanita muscaria* by its strongly striate margin, lack of any trace of a ring, its red flesh beneath the cuticle, and smaller stature.

Cap 1 to 3 inches broad, red, paler when faded in age, with a few yellowish scales. Odor and taste mild. Gills white to yellow, broad, crowded. Stalk 3 to 6 inches long, yellowish-powdery, more or less bulbous. Ring none. Volva consisting of fragile, disappearing particles at the base of the stalk. Spores white in mass.

In deciduous woods, June to September, mostly at lower elevations, but at times up to 5000 feet. It has been found at Cataloochee, Cosby, Heintooga Overlook, near Gatlinburg, and in Cades Cove.

1f   *Amanita brunnescens*

BROWNING AMANITA   UNDOUBTEDLY POISONOUS

Cap 1½ to 3½ inches broad, the color brownish or smoky, at times pallid, disk often darker, margin usually paler, the surface at times with a few whitish or dingy scales. Odor more or less nauseous. Gills white, close, medium broad. Stalk 2 to 5 inches long, often tapering upward, with a ring above, the base bearing a longitudinally-split, grooved bulb, the volva forming a very shallow cup if any at all. Spores white in mass.

Amanita brunnescens is common and widespread in deciduous and mixed woods of the Park. It has been collected in June, July, and August on Rich Mountain, in Cades Cove, at Cherokee, and Indian Creek.

For many years American mycologists mistakenly called this species *Amanita phalloides*. However, the true European *Amanita phalloides*, a greenish or yellowish-olive species, apparently does not occur in eastern North America.

Figure 1f, about one-half natural size

18   *Amanita caesarea*

CAESAR'S MUSHROOM   EDIBLE

Caesar's mushroom, one of the common and strikingly-colored mushrooms of the Smokies, may be sought in both deciduous and coniferous woods in midsummer. Once I found a fairy ring about sixty feet in diameter, consisting of some two hundred fruiting bodies.

Edible and highly prized from ancient Roman days, it has been called the imperial mushroom, the food of the gods. Cicero and Pliny even discoursed upon it. Caution should be taken that it not be confused with the poisonous *Amanita muscaria*, the fly mushroom. The latter species lacks, at the base of the stalk, the deep membranous volva which characterizes *Amanita caesarea*.

Cap 2 to 5 inches broad, various shades of red or or-

ange—the paler colors appearing with maturity—without scales, margin striate. Odor and taste mild. Gills white to yellowish, close, medium broad. Stalk 4 to 7 inches long, whitish to salmon-orange or yellowish; veil forming a yellowish ring (annulus); base of stalk with a rather deep, white cuplike volva. Spores white in mass.

On soil, in deciduous and mixed woods, near Mt. Le Conte, Bullhead, Cosby, Indian Creek, and Cades Cove, July and August.

Figures 1g, buttons, left, and mature mushrooms, below, about two-thirds natural size

Figure 1h, about three-fourths natural size

1h *Amanita rubescens*

THE BLUSHING AMANITA   EDIBLE, BUT USE CAUTION

Cap 2 to 6 inches broad, dingy reddish-brown, more rarely orange-cinnamon, reddish where bruised, with numerous whitish or pale-red scales. Odor and taste mild. Gills white, close. Stalk 2 to 6 inches long, tinged reddish, deeper reddish where bruised, bulbous. Ring ample, persistent. Volva leaving fragments on the bulb and scales on the cap. Spores white in mass

In open deciduous and mixed woods, summer and early autumn, June to October. It is edible, but because of possible mistaken identity it should not be eaten. It has been observed from Cades Cove and Rich Mountain to Cosby.

1i *Amanita mappa*

Some American authors say that *Amanita mappa* is poisonous, but English writers have recently stated that until about twenty years ago it was regarded as poisonous; now, it is said to be perfectly safe but not of good flavor. It is safer, therefore, to avoid eating it.

Cap 1½ to 3 inches broad, yellow with a tinge of green, rarely whitish, with white to wine-colored scales. Odor suggesting radish or faintly of chloride of lime. Gills white, close. Stalk 3 to 6 inches long, white, bulbous. Ring tinged yellowish-green, persisting. Volva adhering to the bulb but with a free margin or rim above. In one variety the volva is lavender. Spores white in mass.

In pine and other coniferous woods, at times in deciduous woods, Cosby, Cherokee Orchard, Greenbrier, and Cades Cove, from June through October, more common in the autumn.

Figure 1i, about two-thirds natural size

Figure 1j, about one-half natural size

1j   *Amanita gemmata*

GEMMED AMANITA   EDIBILITY IN DOUBT

Cap ¾ to 2½ inches broad, yellow, with few to many white patchlike scales. Odor and taste usually mild, rarely of radish. Gills white, close. Stalk 3 to 6 inches long, white to pale yellow, bulbous. Ring present or absent; when present, it is white, soon disappearing. Volva white, adhering closely to the bulb. Spores white in mass.

In deciduous and coniferous (including spruce) woods, rarely on lawns, of wide occurrence in the Park: Cades Cove, Mt. Le Conte, Indian Gap, Elkmont, Oconaluftee Ranger Station, from April to August.

1k *Amanita flavoconia*

In the past, this species has been confused with *Amanita frostiana*. In this confused identity, it is unsafe to assume that it is edible.

Cap 1 to 2½ inches broad, cadmium-yellow, with pale-yellow flocculent patches, or scales. Odor and taste mild. Gills white or pale yellow. Stalk 1½ to 5 inches long, yellow, base somewhat bulbous. Ring yellow, at least on the edge. Volva fragile, leaving patches on the pileus and at the base of the stalk. Spores white in mass.

This small, deep-yellow *Amanita* is a rather common sight in coniferous woods of the Park. It has been found in June, July, and August at both low and high elevations, but it is especially conspicuous in spruce or fir woods on Clingmans Dome, Indian Gap, Mt. Le Conte, and in mixed woods on Gregory Bald, Rich Mountain, Cades Cove, Elkmont, and Cosby.

Figure 1k, about two-thirds natural size

Figure 1l, about two-thirds natural size

1l *Amanita muscaria*

THE FLY MUSHROOM   POISONOUS

This is a much discussed mushroom. It is poisonous, and dried bits of the cap or a decoction of it are taken as a stimulant by Asians. It produces illusions and is said to be in demand on certain occasions which call for celebration. In centuries gone by, the fly agaric has been strongly recommended as a remedy for several different maladies. In earlier days at least, it was used for killing flies—whence the name fly mushroom.

Cap 3 to 5 inches or more broad, yellow, orange, or red, with numerous pale-yellow or whitish scales. Odor and taste mild. Gills white, soon yellow, close, broad. Stalk 3 to 6 inches long, yellow, bulbous. Ring fragile, often hanging from the cap-edge. Volva as scales or zones at the top of the bulb, and as scales on the cap. Spores white in mass.

Found in the Park, in open deciduous and coniferous woods, and on banks of road-cuts, June to October. For several successive summers (August and September), it has appeared abundantly on a clay embankment, between Newfound Gap and Smokemont, at 4000 feet.

2

Armillaria

The species of the genus *Armillaria* have white spores, the gills are attached to the stalk, and the inner veil leaves a ring, or annulus, on the stalk. The Armillarias lack a volva, and are thus distinguished from the Amanitas. They are separated from *Lepiota* by their attached gills. The tissue of the stalk is continuous with that of the cap, and the stalk is therefore not readily separable from the cap. In both *Amanita* and *Lepiota* the stalk separates easily from the cap.

There are relatively few species of *Armillaria* known to science. In the Park, a half-dozen species have been found, and four are included in the key. The most common and best-known species is the honey mushroom, A. *mellea*.

Key to Armillaria Species

1. Mushrooms growing in clusters at the base of trees and stumps; cap honey-yellow or brown ....*2a, mellea*
1. Not in clusters 2
   2. Cap up to 14 inches broad, whitish or grayish, stalk stout, pointed, and rooting ....*2c, ventricosa*
   2. Cap usually 3 to 6 inches broad, brownish 3
3. Growing in moss-hummocks, in pine woods; cap yellowish-tan to olive-tan; with an odor and taste of new meal ....*2b, zelleri*
3. Growing on soil, in deep humus, in deciduous woods; cap brownish with purplish tints; odor mild (at times fruity or of radish), taste bitterish ....*2d, caligata*

Figure 2a, about one-half natural size

2a   *Armillaria mellea*

Cap 2 to 5 inches broad, honey-yellow, or brown, usually scaly. Taste bitter to astringent, disappearing when cooked. Gills white then buff or cream, often stained brownish in age, close. Stalk 4 to 8 inches long, usually scaly downward, dingy to brownish, and bearing a conspicuous ring. Spores white in mass.

A late-summer and autumn species, widely distributed in the world. It is commonly found on or at the base of oak, beech, and other deciduous trees and stumps in the Park. It may be expected along the Rainbow Falls Trail to Mt. Le Conte, from August to October, as well as in Cades Cove, on Gregory Bald, and at numerous other stations. It grows in large clusters and produces striking, blackish stringlike rhizomorphs abundantly under the bark—whence it is called the shoestring mushroom. It attacks the roots of both fruit and forest trees and brings about a decline in vigor, retards growth, and kills branches. Ultimately, the tree may die from the attack. This species is one of the common ones which produce luminescence in wood.

Figure 2b, about seven-eighths natural size

2b *Armillaria zelleri*

ZELLER'S ARMILLARIA   EDIBILITY UNKNOWN

Cap 2 to 4 inches broad, center orange-colored to yellowish-tan, the margin olive-tan, becoming somewhat scaly. Odor and taste, when fresh, slightly of new meal. Gills white, becoming ashy, often brown-spotted, close or crowded. Stalk ¾ to 2 inches long, with one to three rusty-brown zones. The veil forms a flaring, then collapsed, ring. Spores white in mass.

An autumn species, first described as a species new to science from the Pacific Northwest, by Smith and Stuntz, in Smith's *Mushrooms in Their Natural Habitats,* 1949. It was almost simultaneously discovered in East Tennessee. It grows in moss and lichen beds in pine woods. It has been found growing as arcs or fairy rings up to eight feet in diameter.

The first record of it in the Park comes from a collection in Cades Cove, in November, 1957. It may prove to be more generally distributed over the Park than is now known.

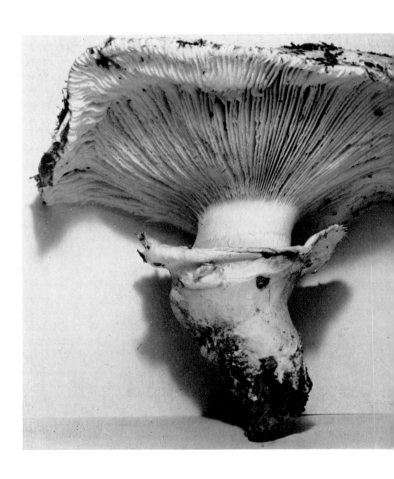

2c *Armillaria ventricosa (Catathelasma ventricosum)*

SWOLLEN-STALKED ARMILLARIA   EDIBLE

Cap 4 to 14 inches broad, whitish or silvery-gray to dingy-gray, shining, smooth. Odor and taste like new meal. Gills white becoming buff, decurrent, narrow, crowded. Stalk 2½ to 6 inches long, stout and somewhat enlarged midway (ventricose), base pointed and rooting. The veil is conspicuous and breaks to form a flaring ring. Spores white in mass.

An autumn species, in pine woods, found over much of the Southeast, and scattered at lower elevations. It has been found in Cades Cove, under pine and hemlock, at times under rhododendron, in October and November. It is one of the largest mushrooms in the Park. When it is cooked, the taste is reported to be agreeable.

More recently this species has been called *Catathelasma ventricosum*, and may be so listed in publications of the last few years.

Figures 2c, left, mature mushroom about one-half natural size; below, young plants about one-third natural size

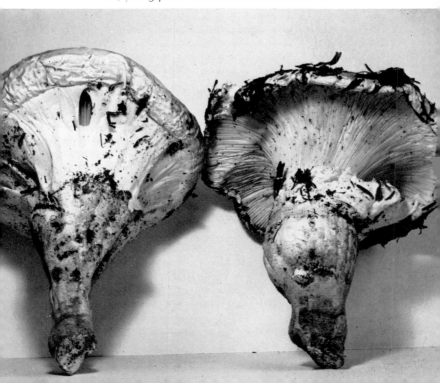

Figure 2d, about two-thirds natural size

2d   *Armillaria caligata*

THE BOOTED ARMILLARIA   EDIBLE

Cap 2 to 6 inches broad, with dark reddish-brown scales which are tinged purplish or wine-colored, whitish between the scales. Odor mild or aromatic, slightly of fruit or at times of radish; taste bitterish. Gills white to grayish, brownish in age, crowded. Stalk 1½ to 3 inches long, brownish and scaly below, white and smooth above, bearing a conspicuous, flaring ring. Spores white in mass.

This *Armillaria* should be looked for in the autumn at the lower elevations. I have found it abundantly only in Cades Cove, in the humus of a deciduous woods, under a huckleberry thicket. These collections were made in October.

3
Lepiota

In the course of a normal growing season, one may expect to find several species of *Lepiota*. To date, thirty species have been collected in the Park.

In the Lepiotas, the stalk breaks easily from the cap; all have a ring, or annulus, and none has a volva. The gills do not reach the stalk—they are free. The spores, in most species, are white or pale cream in mass, but in Morgan's *Lepiota*, the gills and spores are green—whence it is called green-gilled *Lepiota*.

Five species have been selected for inclusion in the key, among which the parasol mushroom and the green-gilled *Lepiota* are the popularly known species.

Key to Lepiota Species

1. Gills white, becoming green at maturity . . . .
. . . . *3a, molybdites*
1. Gills white; if finally colored, not green 2
  2. Cap white or whitish 3
  2. Cap brownish, at least with brownish scales 4
3. Cap white or whitish, mealy, growing in clusters on or about decaying vegetable matter (at times in greenhouses) . . . . *3b, cepaestipes*
3. Cap white, not growing in clusters, scattered on lawns and in pastures . . . . *3c, naucina*
  4. Cap with brownish, somewhat flat scales; gills white, then pinkish, finally brownish; stalk very long (up to 9 inches), scaly below; ring soon movable, like a bracelet . . . . *3d, procera*
  4. Cap with dark, pointed warts; gills white, then pale cream; stalk moderately long or short, silky; ring not movable . . . . *3e, acutaesquamosa*

Figure 3a, about one-third natural size

$3a$ *Lepiota molybdites* (*Lepiota morgani*)

GREEN-GILLED LEPIOTA   POISONOUS

Cap 3 to 8 inches broad, buff, with numerous, pale-brownish scales. Odor and taste slight. Gills whitish becoming dull green. Stalk 3 to 8 inches long, base bulbous, smoky. Ring whitish, becoming movable. Spores green in mass.

In pastures and on lawns, at times as fairy rings (in one instance, the ring in a pasture near Nashville, Tennessee, was twenty-seven feet in diameter); July to September.

This species, more commonly called Morgan's *Lepiota*, has been found in pastures, in Cades Cove, in July and August, but it is met with more frequently outside the Park. It is a handsome, rather large, tempting mushroom. But even so, it should never be eaten. It causes serious illness, and one death is on record, despite the fact that cooking seems to destroy some of its poisonous properties. Its green gills distinguish it, but the collector is warned that the gills are at first white, becoming green only toward or at maturity.

3b *Lepiota cepaestipes*

Cap 1 to 3 inches broad, white, more rarely with a tint of yellow, disk tinged brownish, with numerous grayish soft, more or less mealy scales. Odor and taste slight. Gills whitish or pale cream, crowded. Stalk 2 to 5 inches long, crooked, abruptly enlarged and at times fused, white or tinged cream. Ring white and movable, at times disappearing. Spores white to pale cream in mass.

The striking features are its white mealy caps and its habit of growing in graceful clusters. It may be expected to appear around trash piles, compost, sawdust, straw piles, and rotting logs and stumps. Limited collections in the Park have been made in August, but it might also appear from June to October.

This *Lepiota* gets its name, *cepaestipes*, from the swollen base of the stalk, suggesting an onion set. It is said to be tender and delicious when cooked.

Figure 3b, about two-thirds natural size

3c   *Lepiota naucina*

Cap 1½ to 4 inches broad, white, central portion at times smoky, rarely scaly, more often smooth. Odor and taste mild. Gills free, close, white at first, later pinkish, finally grayish wine-colored. Stalk 1½ to 4 inches long, white, base with a bulb. Ring white, persisting. Spores white, at times tinged cream or pale-pinkish.

The smooth *Lepiota* has not been found in the Park. It will most certainly be discovered there before long, since it is conspicuous, and is common outside the Park on lawns and in pastures in September to November. It is edible, but writers agree that it is easy for the beginner to confuse it with the poisonous *Amanita verna*. In *Lepiota naucina* there is no volva; in *Amanita verna* there is a volva in the form of a membranous cup.

Figure 3c, about three-fourths natural size

3d *Lepiota procera*

PARASOL MUSHROOM   EDIBLE

Cap 2½ to 5½ inches broad, reddish-brown to smoky, the cuticle breaking to form more or less concentric, brown scales. Odor and taste mild. Gills free, close, white then pinkish or brownish. Stalk 6 to 9 inches long, with brownish scales, the base bulbous. Ring soon movable. Spores white in mass.

In open woods, on lawns, and in pastures. It has been collected at Spence Field on Thunderhead, in Cades Cove, and at Meigs Creek, all in August. It may be expected in the Park from June to October.

The parasol mushroom is reportedly fine eating. It is said to be intolerant of shade, a fact which accounts for its habitat.

Figure 3d, about one-half natural size

Figure 3e, about three-fourths natural size

3e   *Lepiota acutaesquamosa*

SHARP-SCALED LEPIOTA   EDIBLE

Cap 1½ to 4 inches broad, pallid-brownish, with numerous dark-brown, pyramidal warts which may be arranged in circles. Odor and taste mild or slightly alkaline. Gills white then pale cream, narrow, crowded. Stalk 2 to 6 inches long, dingy tawny-colored. Ring somewhat cottony, scaly below and on the margin. Spores white to pale cream in mass.

The sharp-scaled *Lepiota* is said to be of excellent flavor.

It has been found in deciduous and mixed woods, and on sawdust, in the Indian Creek area, and along the Rainbow Falls Trail on the north side of Mt. Le Conte, from August through October.

4

Pleurotus

The best-known species in this group is the oyster mushroom, *Pleurotus ostreatus*. This species, however, has not yet been found in the Park.

The more common *Pleuroti* are conspicuous and grow on trunks, logs, and stumps. They are laterally attached to the substratum, often with only a very short stalk, or no stalk at all. The spores in mass vary in color according to the species; they may be white, lilac, or pinkish.

There are only a few species in the Park, of which three common and conspicuous ones are included in the key.

Key to Pleurotus Species

1. Cap hairy, orange to buff; gills orange .... *4a, nidulans*
1. Cap smooth, whitish, grayish, or pale brown 2
    2. Cap usually 3 to 8 inches broad, dingy-whitish or darker (cinnamon-buff, drab, grayish-brown); stalk short; found at lower elevations on deciduous trees, logs, and stumps .... *4b, sapidus*
    2. Cap usually 3 inches or less in diameter, snow white; stalk none; found at higher elevations chiefly on spruce and fir .... *4c, porrigens*

Figures 4a, above, about one-third natural size; right, about one-fourth natural size (photographs courtesy of S. A. Cain)

4a   *Pleurotus nidulans*

NEST-CAP MUSHROOM   EDIBLE, POOR QUALITY

Cap 1 to 3 inches broad, shelving, orange to buff, with dense, white hairs. Odor and taste strong and disagreeable. Gills orange. Stalk none or very short, the cap laterally attached to the substratum. Spores pink to vinaceous-buff in mass.

Although this beautiful mushroom has not been found within the Park, it undoubtedly grows there. It appears in clusters or scattered on trunks, logs, and stumps of both deciduous and coniferous trees. It may be expected to appear from summer through fall and winter.

Because of its disagreeable taste it is undesirable for eating. In much of the literature it is listed as *Claudopus nidulans*.

4b *Pleurotus sapidus*

Cap 1 to 8 inches broad, shelving, whitish, ashy-gray, to grayish-brown, at times with a dull-lilac tint. Odor and taste mild. Gills whitish, extending down the stalk. Stalk short, stout, tomentose, lateral or eccentric. Spores lilac or wine-colored in mass.

Often the savory *Pleurotus* is found in large numbers on logs and stumps of beech, birch, and oak, from July to October. It has been collected around Elkmont, Indian Gap, and Greenbrier.

It is closely related to the oyster mushroom, *Pleurotus ostreatus*, which may occur in the Park. All my collections thus far have lilac spores, whereas in the oyster mushroom the spores are white.

It is of good flavor.

4c *Pleurotus porrigens*

Cap 1 to 3 inches broad, white, more or less wedge-shaped and attached laterally to wood; there is no stalk. Odor and taste mild. Gills white, becoming pale cream, narrow, close. The spores are probably white.

This is a conspicuous, snow-white mushroom which appears abundantly in the dense woods. It is found every year, August to October, at higher elevations, on the trunks and logs of hemlock, fir, spruce, and birch. It may be expected at Clingmans Dome, Collins Gap, Indian Gap, Newfound Gap, Alum Cave Parking Area, and the Chimneys.

Figure 4b, about two-thirds natural size
(*photograph courtesy of A. J. Sharp*)

Figure 4c, about three-fourths natural size

Gills, as illustrated in the detail of Hygrophorus conicus, are the chief distinguishing characteristic of this genus.

5

Hygrophorus

In this genus, the spores are white, and the stalk does not separate easily from the cap. At the very first, beginners may have difficulty in recognizing an *Hygrophorus*. A little experience, however, will overcome this problem. The chief distinguishing characteristic of this group lies in the gills: they are soft and waxy, their edges are sharp, and they are broadened upward toward the cap. Often, indeed, they are spaced widely, distant or subdistant, and usually present a clean appearance.

Thus far some forty-five species of *Hygrophorus* have been listed for the Park, of which nine representatives are presented in the key.

Key to Hygrophorus Species

1. Cap some shade of red or yellow 2
1. Cap of other colors 6
  2. Cap, gills, and stalk soon blackening when handled
    or bruised; the cap conic . . . . *5a, conicus*
  2. Cap, gills, and stalk not blackening 3
3. Cap viscid or glutinous 4
3. Cap moist but neither viscid nor glutinous; stalk dry . . 5
  4. Stalk glutinous; cap convex to plane, variable in
    color, at times pale greenish-yellow, or tinged orange
    or more rarely red . . . . *5b, hypothejus*
  4. Stalk moist, not glutinous, cap conic, scarlet-red, at
    times fading to reddish-orange . . . . . . *5c, cuspidatus*
5. Cap depressed in the center, reddish, fading to yellowish-orange; stalk slender . . . . *5d, miniatus*
5. Cap not depressed, scarlet and fading only slightly;
  stalk relatively thick (⅓ of an inch) . . . . *5f, coccineus*
  6. Cap fawn, clay, or tan-colored, viscid, taste bitter;
    stalk stout, dry, tapering at the base . . . .
    . . . . *5e, tennesseensis*
  6. Cap colors and taste not as above 7
7. Cap coral pink or shrimp pink, viscid; gills white, becoming pinkish, then spotted wine-colored; stalk stout,
  dry . . . .*5g, russula*
7. Cap and gills not as above 8
  8. Cap pale clay to dilute wine-colored, gluten color-
    less, becoming smoky; gills white, becoming greenish-
    spotted; gluten leaving dingy bands at the base of
    the stalk . . . . *5h, paludosus*
  8. Cap and gills not as above 9
9. Cap glutinous or viscid, variable in color: olive-brown,
  often with tints and shades of yellow, orange, or reddish,
  the colors becoming brighter yellow in age; gills white,
  becoming yellow; stalk glutinous . . . . . . *5b, hypothejus*
9. Cap glutinous, clove-brown; gills white, becoming ivory;
  stalk glutinous . . . . *5i, fuligineus*

5a *Hygrophorus conicus*

CONIC HYGROPHORUS   POISONOUS

Cap 1 to 2½ inches broad, moist, more or less sharply conic, red, reddish-orange to yellowish-orange, often with olive tints, more rarely citron-green, becoming black on bruising or in age. Odor and taste mild. Gills at first white, becoming olive, orange, or yellowish, black where bruised. Stalk 2 to 4 inches long, often twisted lengthwise, base white, elsewhere colored more or less like the pileus, black where bruised. Spores probably white.

The distinctive characters are its red to yellow colors, and its blackening throughout when handled, or in age or when dried. Students of mushrooms disagree as to its edibility; some report it edible, others say it is poisonous. It should therefore not be eaten.

Several collections have been taken in the Park: from Cades Cove to Greenbrier, Mt. Le Conte to Indian Creek, in April, and July to October.

Figure 5a, about natural size

Figure 5b, about natural size

5b *Hygrophorus hypothejus*

OLIVE-GLUTINOUS HYGROPHORUS   EDIBLE

Cap ¾ to 3 inches broad, glutinous, color variable: yellowish, orange, or brown, rarely scarlet, the colors becoming brighter yellow in age. Odor and taste not distinctive. Gills white, then yellow. Stalk 3 to 6 inches long, at times shorter, glutinous, whitish or yellowish. Veil leaving a quickly disappearing ring.

This *Hygrophorus* has been found once in the Park, in Cades Cove, in December. It grows in pine woods and has been found only after the season of frosts and freezing weather. Like *H. fuligineus*, it has a thick layer of gluten on the cap and stalk. The odd name, *hypothejus*, is derived from the sulfur-yellow colors under the gluten.

5c *Hygrophorus cuspidatus*

POINTED HYGROPHORUS   EDIBILITY UNKNOWN

Cap ¾ to 2 inches broad, conic, glutinous, scarlet-red. Odor and taste not distinctive. Gills yellowish. Stalk 2 to 3½ inches or more in length, moist but not viscid, yellow, base white. Spores white in mass.

The scarlet-red, pointed caps are a distinctive feature of *H. cuspidatus*. It has been collected in July and August at widely-separated stations, including Cades Cove, Rich Mountain, and Elkmont. It may be looked for in either deciduous or coniferous woods.

Figure 5c, about natural size

Figure 5d, slightly larger than natural size

5d   *Hygrophorus miniatus*

BRIGHT RED HYGROPHORUS   EDIBLE

Cap ⅓ to 1½ inches broad, moist but not viscid, red or scarlet, fading to orange or yellow, the center depressed. Odor and taste not distinctive. Gills broad, colored more or less like the pileus or paler. Stalk 1 to 2 inches long, slender, colored like the pileus, fading slowly or not at all. Spores probably white.

Many collections have been taken from Cades Cove, Bote Mountain, Elkmont, at the base of Mt. Le Conte, Greenbrier, Spruce Flats; in fact, it may be expected anywhere in the Park at elevations below 3000 feet, June to October. It generally grows on soil, in deciduous and mixed woods, but a few times it has been found growing on old, moss-covered logs (at Indian Creek and Cades Cove). It shows a strong tendency toward a gregarious habit of growth. Some collectors report it to be of excellent flavor.

Figure 5e, about two-thirds natural size

5e *Hygrophorus tennesseensis*

TENNESSEE HYGROPHORUS   EDIBILITY UNKNOWN

Cap 2 to 5 inches broad, tawny, clay, or fawn color, viscid. Odor resembling raw potatoes, taste bitter. Gills white. Stalk 2 to 4 inches long, white or dingy, dry, more or less crooked, tapering downward.

The Tennessee *Hygrophorus* appears in abundance each normally wet year, in September to November, in Cades Cove. It was first found in pine woods, near the picnic area, which is on the left as the Cove is entered. This first collection, made on October 17, 1937, was described and published as new to science, in the journal known as *Lloydia*, volume 2, for 1939. Since 1937, it has also been collected above Gatlinburg, near the Cherokee Orchard, and at Tremont. It may be expected under pine or hemlock. Its edibility has not been tested.

Figure 5f, about three-fourths natural size

5f   *Hygrophorus coccineus*

SCARLET HYGROPHORUS   EDIBLE

Cap 1 to 2 inches broad, scarlet-red, fading somewhat, moist, not viscid. Odor and taste mild. Gills red-orange or yellow-orange. Stalk 1 to 3 inches long, dry, colored like the cap, base white or yellow. Spores white.

The scarlet *Hygrophorus* is larger than *H. miniatus*, and its scarlet-red cap is a different shade of red from the red-lead color of *H. miniatus*.

It grows from June to October in low, wet, often grassy, deciduous or mixed woods. Indian Creek, Greenbrier, and Cades Cove have yielded beautiful specimens.

5g *Hygrophorus russula*

Cap 2 to 4½ inches broad, thick and bulky, viscid, shrimp pink, coral pink, usually darker in age, at times with purplish tints. Odor and taste mild. Gills white, soon flushed pink, finally with wine-red spots. Stalk 1 to 3 inches long, stout, dry, white, becoming streaked or tinged pinkish. Spores white in mass.

This large, shrimp-pink or coral-pink mushroom, when found, fully rewards the collector. Like many mushrooms in the Park, it has been found only in Cades Cove. It grows, October through December, in deciduous woods, often oak, or in forests of oak-pine. It is said to be one of the best of the edible mushrooms.

Figure 5g, about three-fourths natural size

5h *Hygrophorus paludosus*

Cap 1½ to 4 inches broad, pale clay or buff to wine-colored, glutinous, streaked or netted beneath the more or less smoky gluten. Odor and taste not distinctive. Gills white, becoming spotted-greenish in age. Stalk 2 to 4½ inches long, glutinous, the dried gluten leaving sordid bands over the lower portion of the stalk, in age the base greenish. Spores white in mass.

Although the name *paludosus* suggests swamp, it has been found only in deciduous woods, in deep humus, Cades Cove, November. Further field work may reveal it in swampy areas.

Figure 5h, about three-fourths natural size

68

5i *Hygrophorus fuligineus*

Cap 1½ to 4 inches broad, clove-brown or darker, center nearly black, heavily glutinous. Odor and taste not distinctive. Gills white to ivory-yellow. Stalk 1½ to 4 inches long, glutinous, whitish. Spores white in mass.

The glutinous substance on the cap and stalk is colorless, and usually very abundant. The gills are beautifully white or ivory. It has been found only in Cades Cove, near Schoolhouse Gap, in deep humus, under pine, hemlock, and rhododendron, in November. The flesh is of fine flavor.

Figure 5i, about two-thirds natural size

6

Laccaria

There are two species of *Laccaria* in the Park, and both are included here: *Laccaria laccata* is common and widespread; the other, *Laccaria ochropurpurea*, is less common, but is striking because of its beautiful purplish gills. A third species, *L. tortilis*, may occur in the Park, but it has not been reported. In *Laccaria*, the gills are waxy, thick at the base (next to the cap), and not close together. Thus, they suggest *Hygrophorus*, but the spores of that genus are smooth, and in *Laccaria* the spores are rough.

Key to Laccaria Species

1. Cap 2 inches or less broad; the gills pinkish or pallid . . . .*6a, laccata*
1. Cap up to 5 inches broad; the gills strikingly purplish . . . .*6b, ochropurpurea*

6a   *Laccaria laccata*

Cap ¾ to 2 inches broad, brown or cinnamon to pinkish-cinnamon, pale when dry, darker when wet, minutely scurfy. Odor and taste mild. Gills broad, distant to subdistant, thick, waxy, with a pinkish tint. Stalk 1 to 3½ inches long, brown. Spores white in mass.

The waxy *Laccaria* is variable in its form; several varieties, based on colors and other characters, have been described. It is said to be of poor flavor and tough texture.

This is one of the most common and widespread mushrooms in the Park. Because of its variation in color and other features, beginners mistake its identity perhaps more than any mushroom in this region. It is found in most any kind of woods, throughout the year, at low elevations, and in the growing season at all elevations.

At times, when conditions favor, it grows in circles—fairy rings, or arcs of circles.

Figure 6a, about three-fourths natural size

6b *Laccaria ochropurpurea*

OCHER-PURPLE LACCARIA

EDIBLE

Cap 2 to 5 inches broad, grayish or pale clay when dry, purplish-brown when wet, glabrous or somewhat scaly. Odor slight, taste disagreeable. Gills bright purplish. Stalk 1½ to 6 inches long, hard, usually paler than the pileus. Spores white with a tint of lilac in mass.

It is said to be very good eating. The disagreeable taste disappears on cooking.

In the Park, the ocher-purple *Laccaria* may be expected to appear from August through October, under pine and hemlock, and in mixed woods, at almost any elevation. Collections of it have been made from Heintooga Overlook, Cucumber Gap, Spruce Flats, Newfound Gap, Indian Gap, and Cades Cove, in August and September.

Figure 6b, about two-thirds natural size

Asterophora lycoperdoides illustrates mushrooms living on another mushroom, a distinguishing characteristic of this genus.

7

Asterophora

Although a majority of mushrooms live on decaying organic matter, a few species lead a parasitic existence on other mushrooms. One of the best-known examples of a mushroom living on another mushroom is the parasitic *Asterophora*.

Figure 7a, about natural size

7a   Asterophora lycoperdoides

PARASITIC ASTEROPHORA   EDIBILITY UNKNOWN

Cap ¼ to ¾ inches broad, whitish becoming dingy or brownish, powdery. Odor and taste like new meal. Gills narrow, thick, whitish or dingy, often not developed. Stalk ¾ to 1½ inches long, whitish then brownish. Spores of two kinds: those on the gills, when developed, are white in mass; and those on the cap-surface are brownish.

This small mushroom is parasitic on species of *Russula*. In the Park, it has been found on *Russula albonigra*, *Russula densifolia*, and *Russula nigricans*. Doubtless, other *Russula* and some *Lactarius* species are also attacked by it. One is fortunate to find it on an average of once yearly. It has been found from August through October in Greenbrier and at Indian Creek. A closely related species, *Asterophora parasitica*, also occurs in the Park. It differs from *A. lycoperdoides* in its smooth spores. The spores are spiny in *A. lycoperdoides*.

8

Cantharellus (Chantarelles)

For years, the Chantarelles have been regarded as true mushrooms. But they have narrow, obtuse gills, and in this respect are unlike other mushrooms. For this and other reasons, they are at times placed in a separate family, near a group known as *Craterellus* (see page 222). In this genus (*Craterellus*), the gills are reduced to mere wrinkles or may be entirely absent. But the Chantarelles are fleshy and soft, and display a habit of growth which would justify their inclusion in this discourse.

Ten species of *Cantharellus* have been found in the Park, four of which are included in the following key.

Key to Cantharellus Species

1. Cap, gills, and stalk yellow throughout, the stalk sometimes pale .... *8a, cibarius*
1. Cap and other parts not yellow 2
   2. Cap and stalk vermilion-red ...... *8b, cinnabarinus*
   2. Cap and stalk not so colored 3
3. Cap deeply funnel-shaped and scaly above (on the inside of the funnel) .... *8c, floccosus*
3. Cap convex, finally only slightly depressed, salmon-orange, becoming purplish where bruised or on handling .... *8d, purpurascens*

8a   *Cantharellus cibarius*

The Chanterelle is one of the well-known edible mushrooms. Its common name is also spelled chantrelle and chantarelle.

Cap ¾ to 3 inches broad, yellowish to buff, fibrillose, becoming glabrous. Odor mild to fragrant, taste mild. Gills yellow, thick, narrow, repeatedly forking, edges blunt. Stalk 1 to 2½ inches long, whitish to buff. Spores pinkish-buff to yellowish in mass.

It grows on the ground in deciduous and coniferous woods, from Greenbrier to the Chimneys, and at White Oak Sinks (Cades Cove area), June through August.

Its yellow color, and blunt, forking gills identify it. The name *cibarius* refers to food; it is famous as an edible mushroom. It resembles closely a relative called *Craterellus cantharellus*, but in this latter one the gills are reduced to ridges or slight wrinkles.

8b   *Cantharellus cinnabarinus*

Cap ½ to 1½ inches broad, scarlet, fading in age or on drying. Odor mild, taste mild or tardily acrid. Gills narrow, ridge-form, forked, red to pinkish-yellow. Stalk ¾ to 1½ inches long, scarlet. Spores pink in mass.

No one should fail to recognize the vermilion chanterelle. Its cap and stalk both are vermilion, or cinnabar-red, in color. They usually grow in large numbers close together. It appears regularly, from June through August, in both deciduous and coniferous woods, and may annually reappear at the same station, at times in arcs or fairy rings.

The acrid taste disappears with cooking, and the flavor is regarded as good.

Figure 8a, about two-thirds natural size

Figure 8b, about five-sixths natural size

8c   *Cantharellus floccosus*

SHAGGY CHANTERELLE   EDIBLE

Cap 2 to 5 inches or more in breadth, deeply funnel-form, orange-rufous, with paler scales. Odor and taste mild. Gills ridgelike or foldlike, forking, pale-yellowish. Stalk ½ to 2 inches long, not distinct from the pileus, light buff. Spores yellowish-cinnamon in mass.

This is one of the curiosities among mushrooms because of its shape. Its surface (inside the funnel) is shaggy from the scales. One should expect to find it in deciduous or mixed woods, at times in rhododendron thickets, from May through September. Once I found it in a pine woods, forming a fairy ring some forty feet in diameter. It may be found at high elevations (4500 feet), or more commonly at lower elevations: Abrams Creek to Indian Creek, Mt. Le Conte, and Greenbrier.

Writers mark this as an edible species for some people; for others, it may cause violent gastrointestinal upsets, despite its delicious flavor.

Figure 8c, about five-sixths natural size

Figure 8d, about three-fourths natural size

8*d* *Cantharellus purpurascens*

PURPLISH CHANTARELLE   EDIBILITY UNKNOWN

Cap 1½ to 4 inches broad, at first convex, finally expanded plane or slightly depressed, salmon-orange, staining purplish when handled. Odor and taste mild. Gills white, purplish when bruised, narrow, close, forked. Stalk 1½ to 4 inches long, salmon-orange, purplish when handled, slightly pointed at the base. Spores honey-yellow in mass.

This is a very rare mushroom, a fact which, alone, justifies its inclusion here. It was first collected in a pine woods, at Indian Creek, near Bryson City, North Carolina, August 11, 1940. It was described as new in the journal *Lloydia*, volume 6, 1943. Although it has been collected repeatedly at this same station, it has not been seen elsewhere in or out of the Park. Its edibility has yet to be tested.

9

Clitocybe

Members of this genus are recognized by their decurrent gills, white spores (rarely colored), and fibrous stalk which does not easily separate from the cap.

There are at least thirty-five species of *Clitocybe* in the Park. Some are white; all others show a rather wide range of colors, including dull grays, gray-browns, clay, buff, cinnamon, yellowish-orange to reddish-orange (in the jack-o'-lantern); more rarely a green *Clitocybe* is encountered.

Two of the more common species are given here.

Key to Clitocybe Species

1. Mushrooms growing in large clusters, generally near oak; cap yellowish, orange, or orange-reddish ....
   ....*9a, illudens*
1. Mushrooms growing scattered; cap grayish, gray-brown, or olive-buff; stalk enlarged at the base ....*9b, clavipes*

9a   *Clitocybe illudens*

JACK-O'-LANTERN   POISONOUS

In darkness, the gills of the fresh specimens of this mushroom are luminescent—whence the popular name jack-o'-lantern.

Cap 2 to 8 inches or more in breadth, golden yellow, reddish-orange, to yellowish-orange. Odor and taste strong and disagreeable. Stalk 4 to 6 inches or more in length, buff-colored, the bases of stalks more or less fused. Spores pale yellow in mass.

The jack-o'-lantern grows in large clusters at the base

Figure 9a, about two-thirds natural size

of stumps of oak and chestnut and other deciduous trees. At times it may be found on the soil, near trees or stumps. The reddish-orange color of this mushroom presents an attractive sight which may be expected from May to October, and one which will not be forgotten. It may be looked for in oak woods anywhere in the Park.

Two other species, *Clitocybe olearia* (from California) and *C. subilludens* (from Florida), are similar to the jack-o'-lantern, and it is possible that the Florida species may occur in the Park. The chief difference lies in the spores of the three species. All three are mildly poisonous, each causing violent vomiting, but recovery of the patient is rapid.

9b *Clitocybe clavipes*

Cap 1 to 3 inches broad, grayish-brown to olive-buff. Odor and taste mild or slight. Gills white then cream-colored. Stalk 1 to 2½ inches long, tapering above the enlarged (clavate) base, whitish to grayish. Spores white in mass.

This species is not infrequent in July, August, and September, but only a few collections have been taken. It is inclined toward spruce and other conifers, but may be found in mixed woods of beech and spruce. It grows at Indian Gap and Tennessee Branch. The grayish tint and the enlarged stalk-base should identify it. As an edible mushroom, some writers report that it is of moderately good flavor; others say it is excellent.

Figure 9b, about four-fifths natural size

10
Xeromphalina

The members of this genus are relatively small in stature, and the species few. Of those species represented in the Park, the most conspicuous is X. *campanella* (more often known as *Omphalia campanella*).

Figure 10a, about natural size

10a Xeromphalina campanella (Omphalia campanella)

BELL-SHAPED MUSHROOM   EDIBLE, FAIR FLAVOR

Cap ¼ to ¾ inches broad, buff, tawny, or rusty-yellow, disk umbilicate-depressed. Odor and taste mild or subalkaline. Gills pale-yellowish, extending down the stalk. Stalk ¾ to 1¼ inches long, date brown, base yellow-hairy, rigid. Spores white in mass.

During the growing season, April to September, one may expect to find rather large clusters of this common mushroom. It has been found on the high mountains growing on fir logs, but it is more frequent on hemlock logs. Collections have come from Cades Cove and Gregory Bald to Indian Gap and Mt. Le Conte.

11

Tricholoma

In this genus the spores are white, the gills are notched at the stalk, and the stalk is not easily separable from the cap. In its notched gills it differs from *Clitocybe* which has decurrent gills. The odor of new meal is present in some species.

A rather large genus in North America, thirty-two species have been found in the Park. Four species are included here.

Key to Tricholoma Species

1. Cap, gills, and stalk white . . . . *11a, resplendens*
1. Not white 2
   2. Cap smoky with a bluish tint, with black radiating fibrils . . . . *11b, portentosum*
   2. Cap with brown or yellow colors 3
3. Cap brown or reddish-tan; gills white, becoming reddish-spotted . . . .*11c, flavobrunneum*
3. Cap center tan-colored and slightly scaly, elsewhere yellow to pale greenish-yellow; gills yellow, not spotted . . . .*11d, flavovirens*

Figure 11a, about two-thirds natural size

11a   *Tricholoma resplendens*

WHITE-SHINING TRICHOLOMA   EDIBLE

Cap 1½ to 4 inches broad, white, viscid. Odor mild or like new meal; taste like new meal, becoming bitter. Gills white, finally flesh-tinted. Stalk 2 to 7 inches long, white, often the base slightly bulbous. Spores white in mass.

This beautiful white mushroom has been found in Cades Cove and on Rich Mountain, in October. It grows in pine and mixed woods, and at first may be hidden by the fallen leaves.

Figure 11b, about two-thirds natural size

11b *Tricholoma portentosum*

DINGY TRICHOLOMA   EDIBLE

Cap 1½ to 4 inches broad, smoky with a bluish or purplish tint, with radiating, black, appressed fibrils. Odor and taste mild. Gills white, often tinged gray to yellow. Stalk 2 to 5 inches long, white. Spores white in mass.

This is one of several winter mushrooms. Although I have gathered it only from Cades Cove, in pine woods, in November, it most certainly grows elsewhere in the Park. Occasionally it forms fairy rings.

McIlvaine says that its caps fried in butter are unsurpassed.

11c Tricholoma flavobrunneum (Tricholoma transmutans)

YELLOWISH-BROWN TRICHOLOMA   EDIBLE

Cap 1½ to 4 inches broad, brown or reddish-tan. Odor like meal; taste mealy-bitter. Gills whitish, becoming reddish-spotted, then brown. Stalk 1½ to 3 inches long, white, with reddish stains and becoming reddish-brown. Spores white in mass.

In late summer and early autumn this mushroom may be found growing in pine and mixed woods. It is not especially attractive because of its dull colors. The gills become reddish-spotted, and the stalk assumes reddish stains.

This is the same as *Tricholoma transmutans*.

Figure 11c, about five-sixths natural size

Figure 11d, about two-thirds natural size

11d Tricholoma flavovirens (Tricholoma equestre)

YELLOWISH-TAWNY TRICHOLOMA   EDIBLE

Cap 2 to 5 inches broad, at times larger, disk tawny and slightly scaly, elsewhere smooth, yellow with a tint of green, and with or without a shade of tan. Odor and taste like new meal. Gills yellow. Stalk 1 to 4 inches long, white or tinged yellow. Spores white in mass.

This is one of our most common and conspicuous winter species of mushrooms. It is usually found in large numbers, scattered through a pine woods. One should look under hummocks of pine needles at the lower elevations. Fine specimens have been found in Cades Cove and near Gatlinburg, in November and December. It sometimes grows in arcs or fairy rings. This mushroom also goes under the name *Tricholoma equestre*.

It is reportedly of good flavor.

12

Lactarius

The spores are white to cream or yellowish, but the distinctive character of *Lactarius* lies in its exudation of a liquid when it is cut, broken, or bruised. Of the one hundred species, or more, now known in the southeastern United States, fifty occur in the Park. The liquid exuded, commonly called milk, or latex, varies in color and behavior with the species. In some the milk is watery; in others it is white and may, in some species, soon change to yellowish, or in other species white and unchanging. In certain species the milk is colored from the first; the striking colors are red and blue. In several species the milk may stain the wounded or bruised portion: in *L. lignyotus*, the milk is white, but it stains the flesh pinkish. In attempting to name *Lactarii*, one must have fresh specimens; when old or dry, they may not exude milk; and color changes, much-needed characters, cannot be observed.

Of the fifty species in the Park, nine are included in the key.

Key to Lactarius Species

1. Cap, gills, and stalk white; the milk very peppery; the gills close and forked ....*12a, piperatus*
1. Not white 2
   2. Cap and stalk dark green; the milk white, becoming buff and staining the white gills green ....*12b, atroviridis*
   2. Not as above 3
3. Cap, gills, and stalk indigo-blue; the milk blue ....*12c, indigo*
3. Not blue 4
   4. Milk dark red; cap smooth, pinkish ....*12d, subpurpureus*
   4. Milk white 5
5. Cap buff, woolly, more or less zoned; milk staining the gills a grayish-wine color ....*12e, speciosus*
5. Not as above 6
   6. Cap conspicuously zoned, color brown or reddish-tan; milk white, unchanging and not staining the gills ....*12f, peckii*
   6. Cap not zoned, color some shade of brown; milk white and, itself, unchanging although it may stain the gills 7
7. Gills close; milk staining the gills brownish ....*12g, volemus*
7. Gills distant 8
   8. Milk staining the gills pinkish; cap dark brown or blackish, margin often scalloped .....*12h, lignyotus*
   8. Milk not staining the gills; cap medium or pale brown ....*12i, gerardii*

12a   *Lactarius piperatus*

PEPPERY LACTARIUS   EDIBLE

Cap 2 to 6 inches or more in diameter, white. Odor slight. Milk white, intensely acrid, not staining the flesh. Gills white, narrow, crowded, forking. Stalk ¾ to 3 inches long, white. Spores white in mass.

The peppery *Lactarius* grows in deciduous woods at lower elevations in the Park during August and September. Often appearing in large numbers after warm rains, it has been collected at Tennessee Branch, Elkmont, and Cades Cove. Its intensely acrid taste disappears with cooking.

Figure 12a, about two-thirds natural size

Figure 12b, about two-thirds natural size

12b *Lactarius atroviridis*

DARK-GREEN LACTARIUS   EDIBILITY UNKNOWN

Cap 2 to 5 inches broad, various shades of dark green. Odor mild; taste mild then acrid. Milk white, becoming buff, usually staining the gills green. Gills white, becoming buff-tinted and staining greenish, narrow, close. Stalk 1 to 3 inches long, rarely longer, green, more or less spotted. Spores whitish in mass.

Although a rather sizable mushroom with a distinctive dark-green color, it is not conspicuous and may be overlooked. It is to be sought in Greenbrier, at the Cherokee Orchard, and in Cades Cove, in either deciduous or coniferous woods, usually in August and September. Its edibility seems not to have been tested.

Figure 12c, about two-thirds natural size

12c   *Lactarius indigo*

BLUE LACTARIUS   EDIBLE

Cap 2 to 6 inches broad, indigo-blue, often with a grayish to whitish luster, more or less zoned. Milk blue. Odor mild, taste soon bitter. Gills blue, at times tinged greenish. Stalk 1 to 3 inches long, blue or pale, at times spotted. Spores cream-colored in mass.

In dense woods this dark-blue mushroom is easily overlooked. Its uniformly blue color, and dark-blue milk make it a unique mushroom. It has been found at several stations (Rich Mountain, Cades Cove, Indian Creek, Forrester Ridge) in pine and mixed woods, August and September.

Since it is reported to be edible, one might assume that the bitter taste disappears on cooking.

12d *Lactarius subpurpureus*

EDIBLE

Cap 1½ to 3½ inches broad, pink, with paler zones, becoming spotted-green. Odor slight, taste bitter to acrid. Gills delicately pinkish-vinaceous, greenish where bruised. Milk red. Stalk 1½ to 3 inches long, pink. Spores pale yellow in mass.

This is one of our more beautifully tinted mushrooms. Its pinkish color, with spots and zones on the cap, and the dark-red milk are characteristic of it. One of its relatives has orange-colored milk.

It grows in pine or hemlock woods, at several stations in the Park, up to 3000 feet or more.

The bitter-acrid taste disappears on cooking.

Figure 12d, about three-fourths natural size

Figure 12e, about two-thirds natural size

12e   *Lactarius speciosus*

THE HANDSOME LACTARIUS   EDIBILITY UNKNOWN

Cap 2 to 3 inches broad, buff, woolly, zoned. Odor mild; taste mild, becoming bitter. Milk white, staining bruised parts grayish-vinaceous, acrid or bitter. Gills white to cream color, stained wine-colored when bruised. Stalk 1 to 2½ inches long, whitish to buff, more or less spotted. Spores white in mass.

This is a handsome, rather rare mushroom. Its zoned, woolly, buff-colored surface, and the grayish-wine stains from the milk make it attractive and easily recognized. I usually find it once or twice each year. It may be expected in July, August, and September, in deciduous woods. It seems to prefer sandy soil. Found near Elkmont and in White Oak Sinks (Cades Cove region of the Park), at 2000 feet or below. I have collected it several times at Highlands, North Carolina, at 3000 to 4000 feet.

12f *Lactarius peckii*

Cap 1½ to 5½ inches broad, tawny to rufous or brownish, conspicuously zoned. Odor mild. Milk white, very acrid! Gills pinkish-cinnamon to brownish. Stalk 1 to 3 inches long, color similar to that of the cap. Spores whitish or pale cream in mass.

The extremely acrid milk has probably deterred my-cophagists from testing its edibility. The Peck *Lactarius* has appeared, from June through September, at several stations scattered over the Park, from 1500 to 4200 feet, from Rich Mountain and Cades Cove to Mt. Le Conte, and from Greenbrier and Cataloochee. It grows in mixed woods, apparently with a preference for conifers.

Figure 12f, about three-fifths natural size

Figure 12g, about three-fourths natural size

12g *Lactarius volemus*

ORANGE-BROWN LACTARIUS   EDIBLE

Cap 2 to 3 inches broad, tawny, golden-tawny, brownish-orange, to cinnamon-rufous, glabrous. Odor strong, taste mild. Milk white, mild, copious, sticky. Gills pale cream, brownish where injured. Stalk 2 to 3 inches long, color similar to that of the cap. Spores white in mass.

In deciduous woods, June to August. It is at times abundant and has been found from Gregory Bald, Cades Cove, and Rich Mountain to Cosby and Greenbrier.

This is one of the better-flavored wild mushrooms. Several authors warn that it must be cooked slowly.

Figure 12h, about natural size

12h   *Lactarius lignyotus*

BROWN-VELVETY LACTARIUS   POISONOUS

Cap 1 to 3 inches broad, dark brown, velvety, rugose. Milk white, staining the flesh pinkish, mild to slightly acrid. Gills white, finally pale cream, pinkish where bruised. Stalk 1½ to 3 inches long, velvety, color similar to that of the cap. Spores white or pale cream in mass.

This mushroom may be looked for in pine, spruce, and fir woods, July through September, from Cades Cove to Cosby, and from Mt. Le Conte to Indian Gap and Indian Creek. The dark colors cause it to be overlooked.

Reports on its edibility are puzzling. Some authorities have found it edible; others say it is poisonous. Possibly individuals vary in their reaction to it. In any event, it is unsafe and should be avoided.

12i *Lactarius gerardii*

GERARD LACTARIUS   EDIBLE

Cap 1 to 3 inches or more in breadth, brown, velvety, radiately wrinkled. Odor mild, taste slightly acrid. Milk white, unchanging, not staining the flesh. Gills white to pale cream, distant. Stalk 1 to 3 inches long, brownish, velvety, often tapering downward. Spores white in mass.

It is reported to be edible, which suggests that cooking removes the slightly acrid taste. Several collections of it have been made in the Park, in July and August, in deciduous and coniferous woods, from low to high elevations, at Cataloochee, Cosby, Mt. Le Conte, Elkmont, Indian Gap, and Clingmans Dome.

Figure 12i, about three-fourths natural size

Russula granulata [not described] is one of more than 60 species of this genus in the Great Smokies.

13

Russula

The Russulas are recognizable by their brittle gills. Another distinctive mark is that the flesh of the cap and stalk is continuous, and therefore these parts of the mushroom do not readily separate.

The cap varies in color from white to dingy, smoky, gray, brown, or even black; or to the brighter colors, greens, yellows, pinks, reds, purples. In no group will one find a greater variety of colors. Ridgway's color book of more than 1400 color charts is at times inadequate when the cap color of a *Russula* is sought.

In serious work with the Russulas one must prepare a spore-deposit to learn the color. In mass, the spores, depending on the species, may be white, pale cream, or deep cream.

In addition to cap and spore colors, the student of Russulas must determine whether the colors of the cap, gills, and stalk change in age or when wounded; he must learn the odor and taste, the kind of markings on the spore-wall; and the detailed structure of the cap-surface.

Before studying the Russulas seriously, I had listed about sixty species in the Park. Now, recent experience with the group indicates that there may be a larger number. In the key, ten species are included.

Key to Russula Species

1. Cap pink or light coral-red, taste very acrid; very fragile . . . . .13b, *fragilis*
1. Cap not pink or red 2
   2. Cap white, without scales .3
   2. Cap not white, or if whitish then scaly 4
3. Gills white, finally pale cream . . . . .13a, *albidula*
3. Gills white, when fresh with a definite tint of blue or blue-green, and stalk with the same blue or blue-green color at the top . . . . .13c, *delica*
   4. Cap ivory-white to flesh-pink, with prominent scales; gills buff or pinkish . . . . .13d, *polyphylla*
   4. Not as above 5
5. Cap with at least some shades or tints of green 6
5. Cap lacking green color 8
   6. Cap finally pale green, with crustlike areas, margin striate . . . . .13e, *crustosa*
   6. Cap not as above 7
7. Cap of one color or mixed: at first wine, lilac, purplish, or greenish, smooth, viscid, margin even; gills repeatedly forked; taste acrid . . . . .13f, *variata*
7. Cap green or gray-green, with soft patchlike scales, dry, margin even to faintly striate in age; gills not repeatedly forked; taste mild . . . . .13g, *virescens*
   8. Cap smoky-gray or dingy gray-brown, finally more or less black; gills and stalk white or pallid but, when wounded, becoming red then black . .13h, *densifolia*
   8. Cap some shade of brown; odor strong 9
9. Cap clay-tan to honey-brown, viscid, margin prominently striate . . . . .13i, *foetens*
9. Cap clay to cinnamon, dry, margin even . . . . .13j, *compacta*

13a   *Russula albidula*

Cap 1½ to 4 inches broad, white, disk buff, viscid when thoroughly wet. Odor mild, taste very acrid. Gills white, becoming pale yellow. Stalk ¾ to 2½ inches long, at times enlarged downward. Spores cream-colored in mass.

A similar white species, also in the Park, *Russula albida*, is mild or slightly bitter to the taste.

Russula albidula has been found in a pine woods, between Gatlinburg and Cherokee Orchard, in July and August.

13b   *Russula fragilis*

Cap 1½ to 2½ inches broad, light coral-red or rosy-pink, viscid, margin striate. Odor mild, taste promptly acrid. Gills white, close, medium broad. Stalk 1 to 3 inches long, white, hollow, fragile. Spores white in mass.

Summer rains usually bring out large numbers of red or pink Russulas. There are many species with differing shades of red colors, and such species are not easily identified. One must have good collections of various stages in development, and in fresh condition. He must then, with a good microscope, determine the kind of markings on the spores, the color of the spores in mass, and also the structural details of the cap.

NO RED, PINK, OR PURPLE RUSSULA SHOULD BE EATEN!

The fragile *Russula* is one of the most common of the red or pink Russulas. It is perhaps the most delicate of all the Russulas. It may be found, June through August, at higher elevations, especially along the state-line ridge, at Newfound Gap and Clingmans Dome, and at Alum Cave Parking Area. It grows in spruce, fir, and hemlock woods, and at times under rhododendron.

A new name attaches it to another species: *Russula emetica* sub-species *fragilis*.

Figure 13a, about two-thirds natural size

Figure 13b, about natural size

13c   *Russula delica*

Cap 2 to 5 inches broad, white, finally with brownish to yellowish stains, at first convex then depressed to funnel-shaped. Odor mild, taste mild to slightly acrid. Gills white, with a tint of blue or blue-green. Stalk ½ to 1½ inches long, white, with a blue-green ring at the top. Spores white or very pale cream.

This all-white mushroom is an interesting find for both the experienced and the novice because of the blue-green tints on the gills and on the stalk next to the cap. It resembles a *Lactarius*, but it lacks milk at any stage. Apparently the slightly acrid taste, if any, disappears with cooking, but it is of moderately good flavor.

It grows, July through October, in coniferous and mixed woods, at scattered points over the Park: Cosby, Greenbrier, Indian Gap, Meigs Creek, and Cades Cove.

Figure 13c, about one-half natural size

Figure 13d, about two-thirds natural size

13d *Russula polyphylla*

MANY-GILLED RUSSULA   EDIBILITY UNKNOWN

Cap 2½ to 6 inches broad, ivory-white, soon tinged buff to pinkish-buff, soon cracking to form reddish-brown scales, margin even. Odor strong, disagreeable, taste somewhat acrid. Gills buff to pinkish, becoming reddish-brown where bruised. Stalk 2 to 3 inches long, whitish, becoming pinkish-brown when handled. Spores white in mass.

This rather large, attractive *Russula* has been found on the Rainbow Falls Trail, Mt. Le Conte, at 3000 feet in mixed woods, in June; and in Cades Cove, at 1800 feet, in mixed woods, in August. So far as known, its edibility has not been tested and reported.

Figure 13e, about two-thirds natural size

13e *Russula crustosa*

ENCRUSTED RUSSULA   EDIBLE

Cap 2½ to 5 inches broad, viscid, greenish, often with straw-colored areas, surface cracked and appearing crusted-scaly, margin striate. Odor mild; taste mild, rarely slightly acrid. Gills white, finally buff. Stalk 1½ to 4 inches long, white. Spores whitish in mass.

This is one of our more common Russulas. It is recognized by its green color with straw-yellowish areas, and by its crusty, cracked surface. It is reported as edible by some writers, but information as to quality of taste seems missing.

It is another of the hundreds of summer mushrooms, found from June through September, in mixed woods, at middle and lower elevations.

13f   *Russula variata*

Cap 2½ to 4½ inches broad, color variable: pinkish or reddish with purplish or green tints, often variegated, at times pale lilac all over. Odor mild, taste acrid. Gills white, repeatedly forking. Stalk 2 to 5 inches long, white. Spores white in mass.

When cooked the sharp taste disappears, and it is then said to be of good flavor.

It may be found at high elevations around Newfound Gap and Alum Cave Parking Area in August, or at lower elevations, 1500 to 2000 feet, from Cataloochee to Cades Cove, June through August.

In recent years, this mushroom has been given a more impressive and also more proper name, *Russula cyano-xantha* variety *variata*.

Figure 13f, about two-thirds natural size

Figure 13g, about three-fourths natural size

13g *Russula virescens*

GREEN RUSSULA   EDIBLE

Cap 1½ to 6 inches broad, green, grayish-green, creamy-green or brownish with an olive tint, with powdery patches or warts. Odor slightly of almonds, taste mild. Gills white, becoming pale buff. Stalk 1 to 3½ inches long, white, rather stout. Spores white.

This *Russula* usually grows singly and has been found from June through August, in deciduous and mixed woods, at both higher and lower elevations: near Gatlinburg and in Cades Cove; at Collins Gap and on the old wagon trail from Indian Gap to the Chimneys.

Although edible, the green *Russula* is not regarded by all as one of the better mushrooms. It is said that it is eaten by squirrels.

Figure 13h, about two-thirds natural size

13h *Russula densifolia*

DENSE-GILLED RUSSULA   EDIBLE

Cap 2 to 5 inches broad, grayish to smoky, finally black-ish. Odor slight or none; taste strong, acrid. Gills crowded, white, becoming sordid-grayish, red then black where bruised. Stalk 1½ to 2½ inches long, whitish, then sordid, red then black where wounded. Spores white in mass.

In coniferous and deciduous woods, June to August, especially at Elkmont, on Rich Mountain, and Cades Cove. Once it was found at Indian Gap under spruce.

Two closely related species in the Park are R. *nigricans* which has distant gills; and R. *albonigra* in which wounded areas become black without first becoming red.

Since it is reported to be edible, there is a possibility that the sharp taste disappears on cooking.

13i   *Russula foetens*

Cap 2 to 5 inches broad, yellowish or honey-colored to dingy clay, with darker stains, margin strongly striate. Odor and taste strong. Gills white, staining brownish where bruised, exuding drops of water in young stages. Stalk 2 to 3½ inches long, white, staining brownish. Spores whitish in mass.

The strong, offensive odor is one important and distinctive mark of the fetid *Russula*. Some writers say it is not edible; others suggest that it is poisonous. The odor and taste would probably deter anyone from eating it.

It is more common in the Park than our records suggest. I have it from Cosby, Elkmont, and Cades Cove, in mixed woods, from July through September.

Figure 13i, about two-thirds natural size

13j   *Russula compacta*

COMPACT RUSSULA   EDIBLE

Cap 2 to 4 inches broad, pale flesh then cinnamon to clay color, dry. Odor strong, and becoming more so on drying; taste mild or tardily acrid. Gills white, becoming brownish where bruised. Stalk ¾ to 2½ inches long, white, staining brownish where bruised. Spores white in mass.

When conditions favor, after summer rains, this mushroom may be expected in oak and mixed woods, from June through September. It has been collected at Newfound Gap, at about 5000 feet, on the north slope of Mt. Le Conte at 3000 feet, and more abundantly at lower elevations around Cosby, Elkmont, and in Cades Cove.

It is edible, but its quality seems not to have been reported. The strong odor on drying, an aid to its identity, may be a deterrent to most mushroom eaters.

Mycena niveipes [not described] is one of the rarer species of Mycena.

14

Mycena

As a group, the Mycenas are small and rather delicate. The spores are white, the cap is often more or less bell-shaped, with its margin straight, not incurved. The beginner may confuse them with *Omphalia* or *Clitocybe*, both of which have decurrent gills. The species of *Collybia* have caps with incurved margins.

Smith in his *North American Species of Mycena* treats two hundred and thirty-two species which grow in the United States and Canada. Some seventy-five species have been found in the Park, including two species new to science: M. *cylindrospora*, found at Alum Cave Parking Area, and M. *setulosa* from along Husky Gap Trail. Neither of these has been reported from any other stations in North America.

In the accompanying key, seven species are included.

Key to Mycena Species

1. Cap, gills, and stalk white; odor and taste mild; caespitose on soil and logs .... *14a, gypsea*
1. Not pure white, although at times fading to whitish .. 2
    2. Cap pink to reddish-purple, fading to whitish; odor and taste like raddish .... *14b, pura*
    2. Not as above 3
3. Stalk exuding a red juice; odor mild, taste mild or faintly bitter .... *14c, haematopus*
3. Stalk not as above 4
    4. Cap yellowish, fading in age or when drying; odor of watermelon rind; growing on the ground in pine woods .... *14d, epipterygia*
    4. Not with these characters 5
5. Cap orange or reddish-orange; gills orange with reddish edges; caespitose on logs .... *14e, leaiana*
5. Cap blackish, brown, or gray 6
    6. Cap at first blackish or dark brown, becoming gray-brown and with reddish-brown spots; gills white to grayish with reddish-brown spots ..... *14f, maculata*
    6. Cap at first watery-gray to smoky, finally pallid to whitish, not spotted; gills whitish or grayish, at times flushed pinkish .... *14g, inclinata*

Figure 14a, about natural size

14a   Mycena gypsea

WHITISH MYCENA   EDIBILITY UNKNOWN

Cap ⅕ to ⅖ inches broad, white or whitish. Odor slight, taste mild or slightly unpleasant. Gills white, medium broad, not crowded. Stalk 1½ to 2 inches long, white, bases white-strigose and fused. Spores probably white in mass.

To date this *Mycena* has not been collected in the Park, but its habitat suggests that it will turn up soon. It grows in white clusters on logs and humus, in deciduous woods, from May to October.

14b   *Mycena pura*

Cap ⅓ to 1⅔ inches broad, rosy, rosy-purple, pinkish-fawn to vinaceous-lilac, at times whitish with a bluish or purplish disk, moist, silky. Odor and taste like radish. Gills whitish, soon pinkish to purplish-drab. Stalk 1 to 4 inches long, concolor with the pileus, base strigose. Spores white in mass.

On humus, in deciduous, coniferous, and mixed woods, from May to November, more common in the autumn. It has once been found on a spruce log, at Indian Gap, in June.

Figure 14b, about three-fourths natural size

Figure 14c, about natural size

14c   *Mycena haematopus*

BLEEDING MYCENA   EDIBLE

Cap ⅓ to 1⅓ inches broad, conic, disk reddish-brown, margin grayish-vinaceous, the flesh exuding a red juice when cut. Odor mild, taste mild or slightly bitter. Gills whitish, staining reddish-brown. Stalk 1 to 3 inches long, shining, exuding a red juice when broken. Spores white in mass.

The bleeding *Mycena* exudes a red juice when broken or cut. It grows singly or in clusters on rotting, often moss-covered logs in coniferous and mixed woods. In July through October, it has been found along the trail from Indian Gap to the Chimneys, and in Greenbrier.

Another species, *Mycena sanguinolenta*, also exudes a red juice, but it is paler and smaller than *M. haematopus*. Still a third one, *M. galopus*, exudes a milky juice, and has a cap which is blackish, fading to gray.

14d   *Mycena epipterygia*

Cap ⅜ to ¾ inches broad, viscid, yellowish, in age with pink or red tints, fading to grayish or whitish, margin striate. Odor fragrant, suggesting watermelon; taste mild or slight. Gills whitish, at times yellowish or flesh-tinted. Stalk 2 to 3½ inches long, slimy, lemon yellow, fading to whitish. Spores white in mass.

Scattered or clustered on soil and humus, in coniferous woods, October to December. It has been found in pine woods, near the Park Headquarters and in Cades Cove.

There is a spring, wood-inhabiting form which grows on pine and spruce logs, at higher elevations, at Indian Gap and Collins Gap, in May and June. This is called *Mycena epipterygia* variety *lignicola*.

If one improvised a common name based on *epipterygia* it would be "winged *Mycena*."

Figure 14d, slightly larger than natural size

Figure 14e, about natural size

14e *Mycena leaiana*

ORANGE MYCENA · · · · · · · · · · · · · · · · · EDIBILITY UNKNOWN

Cap ⅓ to 1⅓ inches broad, orange-red, fading in age and dry weather, glutinous. Odor slightly farinaceous, taste slight. Gills orange-yellow, the edges brilliant reddish-orange. Stalk ¾ to 1½ inches long, yellowish, viscid or lubricous. Spores probably white.

The orange clusters of this mushroom on logs, fallen limbs, and stumps are always an attractive sight. The bright gills with their reddish-orange edges add to the picture. It may be expected at the higher elevations, Indian Gap, Alum Cave, Clingmans Dome, Beech Gap, and Spruce Flats, as well as at Flat Creek and Greenbrier. All collections have been made in May and June on beech, birch, and conifers.

14f *Mycena maculata*

SPOTTED MYCENA   EDIBILITY UNCERTAIN

Cap ½ to 1½ inches broad, umbonate, center at first blackish, finally fading to brownish or smoky, more or less red-spotted, not viscid, margin striate. Odor and taste slightly of new meal. Gills gray then whitish, reddish-brown where bruised. Stalk 1 to 4 inches long, whitish above, reddish below. Spores probably white.

This species grows in clusters or densely crowded, on coniferous logs. It has been found on Clingmans Dome, Indian Gap, and Mt. Le Conte, on spruce and fir logs, in June; and on hemlock in Greenbrier and Cades Cove in October and November.

Figure 14f, about natural size

Figure 14g, slightly larger than natural size

14g *Mycena inclinata*

INCLINED MYCENA   EDIBILITY UNKNOWN

Cap ⅓ to 1½ inches broad, umbonate, olive-brown or smoky, moist or dry, not viscid, striate to disk. Odor and taste like new meal. Gills white, becoming flesh-tinted and stained brownish. Stalk 1 to 3½ inches long, white above, brown below. Spores white.

This *Mycena* grows in clusters on humus and on logs of deciduous trees, in April, May, and June. It has been found between Gatlinburg and Mt. Le Conte, in Greenbrier, and at Cades Cove and Indian Creek.

15

Collybia

In this genus, the spores are white, the gills are attached to the stalk, the stalk is brittle and separates with difficulty from the cap. It is not easy for the beginner to distinguish a *Collybia* from its near relatives, and the specialist is not always sure. In *Collybia,* the gills may be squarely attached to the stalk, not decurrent as in *Clitocybe*, and not notched as in *Tricholoma. Marasmius* species are at times confused with some of those of *Collybia;* but in *Marasmius* the mushroom can, after being dried, be revived in water. Collybias cannot, as a rule, be so revived.

The name *Collybia* means a small coin, which suggests the size of the cap. In most Collybias the cap is small. As a group, the Collybias are not eagerly sought by the mycophagist.

In the Park there are about thirty-five known species of *Collybia*, eight of which are treated here.

Key to Collybia Species

1. Growing on fallen magnolia "cones"; cap small, white . . . . *15a, conigenoides*

1. Not growing as above 2
   2. Growing in clusters or tufts (caespitose) 3
   2. Growing scattered to gregarious 4

3. Cap viscid or glutinous, margin striate; stalk velvety at maturity . . . . *15b, velutipes*

3. Cap dry, moist, or lubricous (like butter), not viscid, margin even or faintly striate when wet . . *15c, acervata*
   4. Stalk growing from a buried, buff-colored or brownish sclerotium; cap white . . . . *15d, tuberosa*
   4. Not growing from a sclerotium 5

5. Stalk tapering and long-rooting below the soil surface . . . . *15e, radicata*

5. Stalk not with this character 6
   6. Cap, gills, and stalk whitish, soon becoming reddish-brown spotted . . . . *15f, maculata*
   6. Cap, gills, and stalk not spotted and not white . . . 7

7. Cap large, up to 5 inches broad, grayish with radiating sepia fibrils on the cap-surface; stalk usually with a long, white rhizomorph at the base . . . *15g, platyphylla*

7. Cap smaller, up to 2½ inches broad, brown or pale grayish, without radiating fibrils . . . . . . *15h, dryophila*

15a *Collybia conigenoides*

Cap ⅛ to ⅜ inches broad, white to pale buff, disk buff, surface with minute, downy hairs. Odor and taste mild. Gills white, buff or yellowish at maturity. Stalk ¾ to 1½ inches long, whitish above, elsewhere dingy, base tomentose. Spores white in mass.

From August to October, one only need look on fallen magnolia "cones" after rains to find this dainty mushroom. It may be expected anywhere in the Park, coincidental with magnolia. Found at Indian Creek, Greenbrier, Meigs Creek, Tennessee Branch, and on the north slope of Mt. Le Conte. Although it grows in clusters, it is so small that apparently no one has tested its edibility. It may be poisonous, but I find no record on this point.

Figures 15a, left and below, about three-fourths natural size

Figure 15b, about three-fourths natural size

15b   *Collybia velutipes*

VELVETY-STALKED COLLYBIA   EDIBLE

Cap 1 to 2½ inches or more in diameter, very viscid or glutinous, yellowish to tawny, margin striate. Odor nitrous, taste slight. Gills white, finally buff. Stalk 1½ to 4 inches long, dark-brown downward, velvety, bases fused. Spores white in mass.

One should hope to find the velvety-stalked *Collybia* in clusters on or around stumps of deciduous trees, usually during and following cool or cold weather. It is common around Knoxville in midwinter. In the Park, it has been found at the Chimneys (Camp Ground and Parking Area), and on the Indian Gap—Chimneys Trail, in November. I was surprised to find it once in July.

The more generous mycophagist rates the velvety-stalked *Collybia* as excellent eating.

15c *Collybia acervata*

Cap ¾ to 2 inches broad, brown to brownish-buff. Odor and taste mild. Gills white, then pallid or sordid, at times becoming reddish in age. Stalk 1½ to 3 inches or more in length, brown, shining above, bases often fused. Spores white in mass.

In large clusters of fifty or more, on rotting logs of conifers. It has been observed growing on spruce logs at Indian Gap and Heintooga Overlook, in June and July.

It is said to have a slightly bitter taste.

Figure 15c, about three-fourths natural size

15d   *Collybia tuberosa*

SWOLLEN-STALKED COLLYBIA   EDIBILITY UNKNOWN

Cap ⅕ to ⅖ inches broad, white, the center pale-brownish. Odor and taste mild. Gills white, narrow, close or subdistant, many short ones present. Stalk ⅔ to 1 inch long, attached to and growing from a buff or brownish tuber-like sclerotium—a hard fungus structure. Spores white in mass.

This interesting little mushroom grows on other decaying mushrooms, in pine and mixed woods, in September and October. It seems rare, although it may be overlooked, having been collected in a pine woods, midway between Gatlinburg and the Park Headquarters, and also near the Cherokee Orchard in mixed woods.

If the edibility of *C. tuberosa* has been tested, I have not come across a report of it. It is too small to be considered seriously by the mycophagist.

15e   *Collybia radicata*

ROOTING COLLYBIA   EDIBLE

Cap 1 to 6 inches broad, viscid, whitish, smoky, or brown, often radiately wrinkled. Odor and taste mild. Gills white, broad, subdistant. Stalk 4 to 8 inches long, often much longer in deep humus, with a tapering "root." Spores white or pale yellow in mass.

The rooting *Collybia* is less conspicuous than more brightly-colored mushrooms and may be overlooked. It is always an interesting find, because of its long tapering stalk which extends for some distance into the humus and soil. In one collection in very loose soil, the rooting-stalk was twenty-six inches long. Usually, however, it is much shorter. It grows at lower and middle elevations in deciduous woods, often in clearings, May to September.

It is said that, when cooked, it is tough but of good flavor.

Figure 15d, about natural size

Figure 15e, about one-half natural size

Figure 15f, about natural size

15f *Collybia maculata*

SPOTTED COLLYBIA   EDIBLE

Cap ¾ to 3½ inches broad, whitish to pinkish-buff, usually with brown spots and stains. Odor mild, taste bitter. Gills white or flesh-tinted, with reddish-brown stains or spots. Stalk 1 to 4 inches long, white, stained reddish-brown, base hairy. Spores cream-colored in mass.

From June to September, this mushroom may be found along Rabbit Creek in Cades Cove, and also near the highway between Newfound Gap and Indian Gap. It may be looked for in spruce or deciduous woods. Its uniformly whitish to pinkish-buff color is interrupted by reddish-brown spots or stains. When it is cooked, the flavor is below average for mushrooms.

15g *Collybia platyphylla*

BROAD-GILLED COLLYBIA   EDIBLE

Cap 2 to 5 inches broad, at first blackish-brown, becoming grayish-brown and radially streaked with fibrils at maturity. Odor and taste mild. Gills white to pale buff, close, broad, deeply emarginate. Stalk 1½ to 4 inches long, white, usually the base bearing conspicuous, white or yellow rhizomorphs. Spores white in mass.

This is a conspicuous mushroom and one of a few species which has been observed in the Park in every month of the year. (See remarks under *Schizophyllum commune*.) Twenty collections are filed in The University of Tennessee Herbarium, but this number could have been in the hundreds.

It grows on logs and in deep leaf mold of deciduous and coniferous woods. It is widespread in the Park, as it is in the United States and abroad. Even the young caps are of only fair quality for eating.

Figure 15g, about two-thirds natural size

15h *Collybia dryophila*

OAK-LOVING COLLYBIA   EDIBLE

Cap ¾ to 2½ inches broad, dark brown, bay, to reddish-brown, often pale-grayish, margin pale. Odor slight, taste mild. Gills white then buff, narrow, crowded. Stalk 1 to 4½ inches long, whitish to pale-yellowish or clay, often several are fused at the base. Spores white in mass.

It is said to be of good flavor. At times it is abundant, and usually is gregarious or even clustered on leaf mold in deciduous and mixed woods. Collectors are certain, in time, to come upon it growing in arcs or fairy rings. It should be found from May to August, or even later, almost anywhere in the Park. I have it from eight scattered stations, ranging from Heintooga Overlook to Cades Cove.

Figures 15h, left and above, about three-fourths natural size

Figure 15h, about five-sixths natural size

16

Schizophyllum

This genus is represented in the Park by the species *commune*. It may be seen on every trip to the woods. It withstands low temperatures, and, like *Collybia platyphylla*, is found in every month of the year.

The species of this genus always grows on dead limbs and logs of various trees.

Since only one species is known, there is no call for a key.

16a *Schizophyllum commune*

SPLIT-GILLED MUSHROOM   EDIBILITY UNKNOWN

Cap ½ to 1 inch broad, whitish to gray when dry, brownish-gray when wet, hairy, tough, fan-shaped, attached laterally. Gills radiating from the point of attachment, grayish, edges grooved or split. Stalk none. Spores pinkish in mass.

This is one of the most common mushrooms in the Park. Indeed, it has been seen so frequently that I have neglected to bring it to the laboratory. As a result, there are but four collections in the Herbarium of The University of Tennessee, from the Park. On the other hand collections are in the Herbarium from several states, and from Mexico, Guatemala, Canal Zone, and the Philippines. It is certainly world-wide in its occurrence.

The caps, after being dried, revive easily in water. The edges of the gills are grooved—whence the name *Schizophyllum* (split gills).

Figure 16a, about one-half natural size

17

Marasmius

Aside from white spores, *Marasmius* species are tough, only slightly fleshy mushrooms. After being dried they soon revive in water. Because of their tough texture they persist longer than other more fleshy mushrooms.

The reviving character distinguishes *Marasmius* from *Collybia*; otherwise, some species at least are moved back and forth from one genus to the other according to the opinion of the mycologist. To a degree, the same comments apply to *Mycena* and *Marasmius*.

About twenty-five species are known from the Park; there are doubtless another twenty-five still to be recognized from that area. Four of the more common species are included in the key.

Key to Marasmius Species

1. Cap white; growing on sticks ....*17a, candidus*
1. Cap colored 2
    2. Cap rose-madder or reddish-cinnamon ..*17b, siccus*
    2. Cap not so colored; growing in clusters 3
3. Cap pinkish-buff, velvety; odor disagreeable; stalk velvety below, horny ....*17c, cohaerens*
3. Cap white or gray when dry, reddish to brownish when wet; odor mild; stalk white-downy ....*17d, confluens*

Figure 17a, about three-fourths natural size

17a   *Marasmius candidus*

WHITE MARASMIUS   UNEDIBLE

Cap ⅓ to 1⅓ inches broad, white, dry, margin with shallow grooves. Odor and taste slight to farinaceous. Gills white or with a flesh tint, narrow and veinlike, forked, often irregularly branched and then forming a network. Stalk ⅓ to 1½ inches long, apex white, elsewhere blackish, brownish, or whitish. Spores white or pale yellow.

During the summer, in dense woods, the white *Marasmius* is frequently found on fallen twigs, rarely on fallen leaves, and even more rarely on mossy logs. It has been collected at six stations in the western half of the Park, and may be expected everywhere in the Park at the lower elevations (below 3000 feet). Whether it may occur at higher elevations is not on record.

Figure 17b, about natural size

17b *Marasmius siccus*

DRY MARASMIUS   EDIBILITY UNKNOWN

Cap ⅓ to 1½ inches broad, cinnamon-rufous, rosy, or rose-madder, deeply grooved to the disk. Gills white, distant, usually veined at the cap. Stalk 1½ to 4 inches long, horny, brown or blackish, shining. Spores white in mass.

The dry *Marasmius* is one of the most beautiful mushrooms in the Park. Its coloring and trim outlines are arresting features, indeed!

It grows in leaf mold, in deciduous and mixed woods, generally throughout the Park. It has been found along Abrams Creek and in White Oak Sinks (Cades Cove area), on Mt. Le Conte, and at Cherokee, from June to October.

Figure 17c, about natural size

17c   *Marasmius cohaerens*

FUSED MARASMIUS   EDIBLE

    Cap ⅓ to 1⅓ inches broad, pinkish-buff, velvety. Odor and taste strong and disagreeable. Gills whitish to buff, edges purplish-brown. Stalk 2¼ to 4 inches long, bases fused, rigid and horny, reddish-brown, velvety below. Spores white in mass.

    This is found growing in leaf mold, usually in clusters, the bases of the stalks then fused. For several years it has appeared along the Rainbow Falls Trail at 3200 feet, and has also been found generally in the Park from May to September.

17d *Marasmius confluens*

EDIBLE

Cap ¾ to 2¼ inches broad, whitish or grayish when
dry, reddish or brownish when wet. Odor and taste slight
or mild. Gills whitish, narrow, crowded. Stalk 2 to 4½
inches long, densely white-downy, reddish beneath the
hairs, bases white-tomentose, bound together with dead
leaves. Spores white in mass.

The tufted, or confluent, *Marasmius* is encountered at
times in abundance, at both high and low elevations, in
deciduous and coniferous woods. One collection, from near
Heintooga Overlook, in a spruce woods, was growing in
a fairy ring ten feet in diameter. It may be looked for from
July through September.

Figure 17d, about three-fourths natural size

18

Panus

The caps are tough to leathery, and they revive in water after being dried. The spores are white or tinged yellow to buff. The stalks are often lateral, and may be short or absent altogether.

Fries, the great Swedish mycologist, says that the name *Panus* was used by Pliny for a tree-inhabiting fungus.

There are approximately thirteen species in the southeastern United States, about half of which are found in the Park, and three are included here.

Key to Panus Species

1. Cap ½ inch or less in diameter, grayish or cinnamon; flesh with an astringent taste . . . .*18a, stypticus*
1. Cap larger; taste not astringent 2
    2. Cap large (up to 10 inches broad), white, with prominent, lateral stalk . . . .*18b, levis*
    2. Cap 1 to 4 inches broad, clay color to tawny-olive when dry, with violaceous tints when wet, coarsely hairy; stalk short, lateral to eccentric . . . .*18c, rudis*

Figure 18a, about natural size

18a   *Panus stypticus*

ASTRINGENT PANUS   POISONOUS

Cap ¼ to ½ inch broad, grayish when dry, cinnamon when wet, surface breaking up to form minute, powdery or scurfy scales. Odor mild, taste astringent. Gills pale-brownish, close, at times forked. Stalk lateral, very short, ¼ of an inch or less in length, at times apparently absent. Spores white in mass.

This is almost world-wide in occurrence, and very common in the eastern United States. In spite of its prevalence, I have but four collections from the Park: from Greenbrier, Elkmont, Rich Mountain, and Cades Cove.

This *Panus* is small but abundant and rather conspicuous. In some forms of it, the gills give off a soft glow (luminescence), after ten or fifteen minutes in the dark. The British form is said not to be luminescent.

The unpleasant, astringent taste would deter most mycophagists from eating it. It is said to be poisonous. The sour taste is prompt and seems permanent—at any rate it is lingering!

18b   *Panus levis*

Cap 3 to 10 inches broad, at first white, finally yellowish, the margin at first fringed. Odor mild, or of chloride of lime, taste mild. Gills white becoming yellowish. Stalk 2 to 5 inches long, stout, central or eccentric, white, yellow-strigose especially at the base. Veil observed in the young stages, leaving remains on the margin of the cap. Spores white to pale buff in mass.

In its best state, this is one of the beautiful white mushrooms of the Park. One is fortunate to find it in such excellent state of development as shown in the accompanying illustration.

It has been found once in Cades Cove on oak, and once on apple, in an old orchard near the Park Headquarters, both collected in August. It is said to have fair flavor.

Figure 18b, about one-half natural size

Figure 18c, right, about one-third natural size

18c   *Panus rudis*

ROUGH PANUS   EDIBLE

Cap 1 to 4 inches broad, tough and leathery, olive-tan to pale-clay color, often violaceous when wet, more or less densely covered with coarse white hairs. Odor mild; taste mild, but soon bitter. Gills white to pale cream, violaceous when wet, very narrow, crowded, forking. Stalk central or eccentric, with coarse hairs. Spores white or yellowish.

It grows in large numbers (scores or a few hundred) on stumps and logs.

This is a common and widespread mushroom, although I have but two collections from the Park: from Newfound Gap at 5000 feet, on a pine stump in July, and from Gregory Bald at 4000 feet in July. It is common about Knoxville on stumps of deciduous trees. I have it in the Herbarium of The University of Tennessee, from Alabama, North Carolina, Florida, Louisiana, and Indiana, as well as from Oaxaca, Mexico, and Panama. It seems to be world-wide.

The bitter taste disappears on cooking. It is less tough when young, and at all stages is said to give a good flavor to gravy.

19

Pluteus

To the experienced student this is a distinct and easily recognized genus of mushrooms. It has free gills, pink spores, and the stalk has neither ring (annulus) nor volva. Some eight or ten species have been found in the Park, the largest and most conspicuous being *P. cervinus*.

19a *Pluteus cervinus*

Cap 1½ to 5 inches broad, variable but usually brown to smoky-gray, at times whitish, viscid. Odor slight; taste slightly unpleasant, soon bitter. Gills white then flesh-pink. Stalk 3 to 6 inches long, dingy-white, bases often fused. Spores cinnamon or pinkish in mass.

During the summer one should look on old sawdust piles and decaying wood to find this fawn-colored mushroom. It grows singly, but more often in clumps of three to eight specimens. It has been found in Cades Cove in August and at the Chimneys Camp Ground in May.

It is said to be of good flavor. The bitterness is said to disappear on cooking.

Figures 19a, left and below, about two-thirds natural size

20

Clitopilus

The spores are pinkish to rosy, the stalk fleshy, but not brittle, and at times eccentric, and the gills decurrent. There is no volva and no annulus. The odor of new meal is commonly present. There are four, perhaps five, species in the Park, only two of which are included here. A key is hardly necessary.

20a *Clitopilus novaboracensis*

NEW YORK CLITOPILUS   EDIBILITY UNCERTAIN

Cap 1 to 3 inches broad, often concentrically cracked, whitish to ashy, dark-ashy where bruised, margin often cleft. Odor like meal, taste like meal then bitter. Gills decurrent, narrow, close, brownish-ashy. Stalk 1 to 2 inches long, brownish with a whitish coating of fibrils, base more or less bulbous. Spores pinkish in mass.

In one variety the cap is violet-gray; in another the odor is strongly alkaline.

From August to October, the New York *Clitopilus* is found in woods where there is deep humus. It has been found growing in fairy rings, in one instance eight feet in diameter, in another twelve feet in diameter. Stations include Indian Creek, Greenbrier, Mt. Le Conte, and Cades Cove. Because of its warty, angular spores it is sometimes listed by the name *Rhodocybe novaboracensis*.

Figures 20a, left and below, about three-fourths natural size

20b *Clitopilus orcellus*

SWEETBREAD MUSHROOM   EDIBLE

Cap 1 to 3½ inches broad, chalk white, at times slightly smoky. Odor and taste like meal. Gills white, then pinkish-buff, narrow, close. Stalk ¾ to 3 inches long, white, silky. Spores pinkish-brown in mass.

The sweetbread mushroom grows in humus, in deciduous woods, at times in arcs or circles (fairy rings). Stations where it has been found include Cataloochee, Indian Creek, Spruce Flats, Meigs Creek, and Cades Cove, from August through October.

It is reportedly excellent eating.

Figure 20b, slightly larger than natural size

Entoloma strictius is one of the more common species of this genus found in the Great Smokies.

21

Entoloma

The spores are pinkish, the stalk fleshy and not easily separable from the cap, the gills typically notched at the stalk and often separating from it.

About eighteen species have been found in the Park. Two of the more common ones are included, without a key.

Figure 21a, about three-fourths natural size

21a   *Entoloma salmoneum*

SALMON-COLORED ENTOLOMA   PROBABLY POISONOUS

Cap ¾ to 2 inches broad, conic-papillate, orange-salmon to apricot-orange, disk at times greenish. Odor and taste mild. Gills orange-salmon. Stalk 2 to 4½ inches long, salmon-colored, often tinged greenish. Spores pinkish-brown in mass.

This species may be a color-form of *Entoloma cuspidatum* which is bright yellow.

The salmon-colored *Entoloma* grows on the ground, in humus, in mixed woods, at times under rhododendron, from July through October. It has been found at Indian Creek, in Greenbrier, on Mt. Le Conte at 5000 feet, and along Bote Mountain Trail to Spence Field (on Thunderhead).

21b *Entoloma strictius*

Cap 2 to 3 inches broad, more or less umbonate, olive-buff to brown. Odor and taste mild or of new meal. Gills pallid, becoming cinnamon. Stalk 2 to 6 inches long, dingy, usually twisted, easily splitting. Spores orange-cinnamon in mass.

In deciduous and coniferous woods, especially at higher elevations, May to September.

Experience indicates that this species grows most commonly at higher elevations. It is not uncommon on Clingmans Dome in fir woods, at 6600 feet, at Indian Gap, on Mt. Le Conte, and along the Bote Mountain Trail to Thunderhead. It has less frequently been found at lower elevations in Cades Cove, Elkmont, and Meigs Creek.

Figure 21b, about three-fourths natural size
(with spore deposit shown at right)

*Nolanea cuspedata [not described] is a strik-
ing mustard-yellow member of the genus
Nolanea.*

22

Nolanea

The name of this genus is derived from the Latin
meaning a little bell. Like *Pluteus*, it has pink spores,
but in *Nolanea* the pileus margin (edge) is at first
straight; in *Pluteus* the margin is at first incurved.
Generally, the species are small, often relatively inconspicuous. From the Park about eight species have been
recorded.

Figure 22a, slightly larger than natural size

22a   *Nolanea fuscogrisella*

SMOKY-GRAY NOLANEA   EDIBILITY UNKNOWN

Cap ¾ to 1¾ inches broad, mouse-colored, with glistening particles, margin radiately furrowed when wet. Gills white to flesh-tinted. Stalk 1 to 2½ inches long, often twisted, mouse-colored. Spores pale cinnamon in mass.

This is one of the less common species in the Park. It has been found along the Indian Gap–Chimneys Trail (old wagon road), and on the north slope of Mt. Le Conte at 3000 feet. It fruits in July and August.

23

Leptonia

The spores are pinkish, the stalk brittle and often hollow, the cap thin and depressed on the center (disk). Often the fibers on the cap separate at the ends which turn up. The gills are attached to the stalk.

All the species in the Park are relatively small and delicate (the name *Leptonia* means slender), and often inconspicuous. Some are beautifully tinted. Few, if any, have been tested for edibility.

Eighteen species have been found in the Park, three of which are included here.

Key to Leptonia Species

1. Cap blue-black all over 2
   2. Stalk blue-black to steel-blue . . . .*23a, lampropa*
   2. Stalk smoky-gray . . . .*23b, serrulata*
1. Cap gray to pinkish-buff; stalk grayish-smoky . . . .
   . . . .*23c, subserrulata*

23a   *Leptonia lampropa*

SLENDER MUSHROOM   EDIBILITY NOT KNOWN

Cap ⅓ to 1⅓ inches broad, depressed, bluish-black or dark slate, fading in age to brownish, with minute scales on the center. Odor mild, taste mild or slightly mealy. Gills attached, white then pinkish. Stalk 1 to 2¾ inches long, bluish-black to steel-blue, base usually white-mycelioid. Spores pink.

It is found growing on leaf mold and on decaying chestnut bark, especially at Indian Creek and along the Rainbow Falls Trail (at 2500 to 3500 feet); also along the Indian Gap–Chimneys Trail, at Flat Creek, and Cades Cove, May to August.

Figure 23a, about three-fourths natural size

Figure 23b, about natural size

23b   *Leptonia serrulata*

TOOTH-GILLED LEPTONIA   EDIBILITY UNKNOWN

Cap ⅓ to 1½ inches broad, depressed, bluish-black fading to grayish-violet, minutely scaly on the disk. Odor and taste mild. Gills pallid then bluish-gray, the edges dark blue and serrulate. Stalk 1½ to 3 inches long, grayish-smoky. Spores pinkish.

Like other Leptonias this one grows in densely shaded woods, in humus and on moss-covered logs, in June, July, August, and September, and has been found at these stations: Tennessee Branch, Indian Creek, Elkmont, Mt. Le Conte, and Cades Cove.

Figure 23c, about natural size

23c   *Leptonia subserrulata*

SLIGHTLY TOOTHED LEPTONIA   EDIBILITY UNKNOWN

Cap ⅓ to 1⅔ inches broad, depressed or umbilicate, grayish to pinkish-buff, blackish at the center. Odor and taste mild or grasslike. Gills white then pinkish, edges blue-black and toothed. Stalk 1 to 3 inches long, grayish or smoky, the apex with bluish-black scales. Spores pinkish.

This *Leptonia* grows on soil, in humus, in Cades Cove, Smokemont, and Indian Creek, in August and September. It somewhat resembles *Leptonia serrulata* in which the cap is blue-black.

24

Paxillus

In the genus *Paxillus*, the gills are decurrent and are easily peeled from the flesh of the cap. The gills also are forked and tend to anastomose on the stalk, if one is present. The spores are olive-buff to greenish in mass.

Five species have been found in the Park, three of which are included in the key.

Key to Paxillus Species

1. Stalk none, the caps attached by one side; gills wavy-corrugated . . . .*24a, curtisii*
1. Stalk present 2
   2. Stalk densely brownish-velvety; cap brownish to buff . . . .*24b, atrotomentosus*
   2. Stalk yellowish, with small scales; cap brownish to orange-cinnamon . . . .*24c, rhodoxanthus*

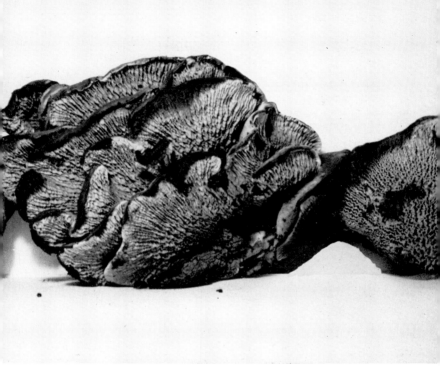

Figure 24a, about natural size

24a   Paxillus curtisii (*Paxillus corrugatus*)

CURTIS' PAXILLUS   EDIBILITY UNKNOWN

Cap ¾ to 2½ inches broad, shelving, yellow, olive, or orange. Odor disagreeable, taste bitter. Gills radiating from a basal-point, corrugated, yellow. Stalk none; caps laterally attached. Spores olive-buff, or rarely honey-yellow in mass.

Four collections have been taken in the Park. It would therefore seem to be a bit rare. These collections were from oak as well as conifers, from June through September, and the stations were: Rich Mountain, Cades Cove, and Greenbrier.

Curtis' *Paxillus* has also been called *Paxillus corrugatus*.

24b *Paxillus atrotomentosus*

BLACK-VELVETY PAXILLUS   EDIBILITY IN DOUBT

Cap 3 to 6 inches broad, rusty-brown to buff. Odor and taste alkaline. Gills buff, easily separable from the cap. Stalk 1 to 3 inches long, eccentric or at times central, densely brownish-velvety. Spores dark olive-buff in mass.

This interesting mushroom grows singly or clustered on hemlock and other conifers, on logs, stumps, and on buried wood, from June through August. Collections have been made from Cades Cove and Abrams Creek (near Chilhowee) to Elkmont and Mt. Le Conte.

Mycologists disagree somewhat as to its edibility: some say it is suspected of being poisonous; others state that it has a marked but pleasant taste; and still others do not regard it as good.

Figure 24b, about one-half natural size

Figure 24c, slightly larger than natural size

24c *Paxillus rhodoxanthus*

YELLOW-ROSE PAXILLUS   EDIBLE

Cap 1½ to 4 inches broad, brown, orange-cinnamon, or reddish-brown, tomentose, surface becoming cracked. Odor and taste mild. Gills yellow. Stalk ¾ to 2½ inches or more in length, yellowish with small russet scales, often tapering below. Spores olive to green in mass.

Most of my collections of the yellow-rose *Paxillus* have come from medium to higher elevations, often above 4000 feet. It has been found in deciduous and mixed woods, from July to September. Stations include Bote Mountain Trail to Thunderhead, Chimneys–Indian Gap Trail, Greenbrier, and Mt. Le Conte.

25

Cortinarius

Smith, in his *Mushrooms in Their Natural Habitats*, says the genus is a paradox in that it is hard to define but easy to recognize. The spores are brown, an inner veil is present and resembles a spider-web, and the flesh of the stalk and cap is continuous. As long as these characters are conspicuous, the beginner should experience little difficulty in placing a species of *Cortinarius* in its proper genus. The veil must be looked for in young mushrooms.

The group is large and is found most abundantly in the late summer and autumn. In the Park, there are more than one hundred named species, and perhaps another fifty awaiting names. Six species are included in the key.

Key to Cortinarius Species

1. Cap color some shade of brown 2
1. Cap color some shade of yellow or buff 4
   2. Odor of radish; growing in spruce and fir woods . . . . 25a, *evernius*
   2. Odor spicy, at least slightly so 3
3. Cap dark brown, scaly; stalk up to 1½ inches broad at the base . . . . 25b, *squamulosus*
3. Cap brown, slightly scaly; stalk equal . . . . . 25c, *distans*
   4. Stalk equal, not bulbous; taste bitter, gills close and narrow . . . . 25d, *vibratilis*
   4. Stalk either bulbous or clavate 5
5. Stalk bulbous; gills medium broad, close, pinkish-buff . . . . 25e, *multiformis*
5. Stalk clavate; gills broad, subdistant, yellowish . . . . 25f, *flavifolius*

25a   *Cortinarius evernius*

Cap 1½ to 5 inches broad, umbonate, brown, radially streaked when drying. Odor and taste of radish. Gills brown, edges pale, broad. Stalk 4 to 8 inches long, cylindric, vinaceous-gray. Veil white, often leaving white patches on stalk. Spores brown in mass.

In July and August, at times in September, one will find this species in the spruce and fir woods atop Mt. Le Conte and Clingmans Dome, and at Indian Gap. It should be looked for especially in deep moss.

Figure 25a, about two-thirds natural size

Figure 25b, about three-fourths natural size

25b   *Cortinarius squamulosus*

SCALY CORTINARIUS   EDIBLE

Cap 2 to 4½ inches broad, russet to brown, scaly. Odor somewhat spicy. Gills emarginate, dark grayish-purple, broad, close. Stalk 3 to 6 inches long, base bulbous, the bulb up to 1½ inches broad, the veil leaving a band-like ring near the top of the stalk. Spores brown in mass.

Because of its dark colors, the scaly *Cortinarius* is inconspicuous and is doubtless often overlooked. It is said to be of fair flavor.

It has been found in both deciduous and mixed woods, in Greenbrier, on the north slope of Mt. Le Conte, and in Cades Cove, in August.

25c *Cortinarius distans*

DISTANT-GILLED CORTINARIUS   EDIBLE

Cap 1 to 3 inches broad, umbonate, brown, minutely scaly. Odor slightly spicy, taste slight. Gills emarginate, pallid then brown, distant, broad. Stalk 2 to 5 inches long, brownish, base enlarged. Veil leaving a broad, white band above on the stalk, and scattered white patches below. Spores brown in mass.

It is edible, but of poor quality.

The distant-gilled *Cortinarius* grows at both low and high elevations: near the Park Headquarters, Indian Creek, Cades Cove, Elkmont, Roaring Fork, Clingmans Dome, in both mixed and coniferous woods, May through September.

One form with lavender gills was found along Roaring Fork.

Figure 25c, about three-fourths natural size

25d *Cortinarius vibratilis*

EDIBILITY UNKNOWN

Cap 1 to 3½ inches broad, buff to maize-yellow, glutinous. Odor pungent, taste bitter. Gills buff to cinnamon. Stalk 2 to 5 inches long, glutinous. Veil weblike, white, becoming brown from the spores. Spores clay-brown in mass.

The extreme bitterness of this mushroom may be demonstrated merely by touching the cap with the tongue.

This species of *Cortinarius* has been found in pine and spruce woods, in each instance in moss-beds, in July and August at Indian Gap (5200 feet), and from August through November in Cades Cove.

Figure 25d, about three-fourths natural size

Figure 25e, about two-thirds natural size

25e   *Cortinarius multiformis*

MANY-FORMED CORTINARIUS   EDIBILITY UNKNOWN

Cap 2 to 4 inches broad, viscid, whitish in the button-stage, then buff with a white bloom, becoming more or less shining and radiately wrinkled. Odor and taste mild. Gills white then slightly darker, close. Stalk 1½ to 3½ inches long, white then yellowish-clay, the base usually with a conspicuous bulb which is margined. Spores brownish in mass.

This *Cortinarius* will be found in late August and September at the higher elevations, and at the lower elevations in the autumn through December. It has been found on Clingmans Dome under fir in September, in Greenbrier and Cades Cove in October in mixed woods.

There is some variation in color but not strikingly greater than in many mushrooms. Thus, the species-name *multiformis* is a bit puzzling.

Figure 25f, about three-fourths natural size

25f *Cortinarius flavifolius*

YELLOW-GILLED CORTINARIUS   EDIBILITY UNKNOWN

Cap 1½ to 3 inches or more in breadth, cream-buff to yellowish-tan, minutely scaly, dry. Odor mild. Gills emarginate, broad, yellow, finally rusty. Stalk 2 to 4 inches long, enlarged at the base. Veil white, silky. Spores brownish in mass.

This is one of several species of *Cortinarius* which grows in deciduous woods. It has been found in Greenbrier and Cades Cove, in September and October.

26

Naematoloma

Most students of fungi may know the members of this group better under the generic name *Hypholoma*. *Naematoloma* is characterized by purple-brown spores, an inner veil which at first clings to the cap-margin (and there is no ring). A volva is also absent.

The genus *Naematoloma* is rather closely related to *Agaricus*, the genus which includes the meadow mushroom, or the commercially-grown mushroom. *Agaricus* has a ring, and its gills are pink.

There are nine species and varieties in the Park, two of which are included in the key.

Key to Naematoloma Species

1. Disk of cap brick-red; gills not becoming green; taste mild ....26a, *sublateritium*
1. Disk of cap buff-colored; gills becoming green; taste bitter ....26b, *fasciculare*

26a *Naematoloma sublateritium*

Cap ¾ to 2½ inches broad, honey-yellow, cinnamon-rufous, to chestnut, disk brick-red, margin often fringed from the veil. Odor and taste mild. Gills whitish then pale olive-gray. Stalk 1 to 2½ inches long, dingy below, pallid above. Veil whitish to pale-yellowish, soon disappearing. Spores purplish-brown in mass.

A distinguishing characteristic is the brick-red color of the disk. It also lacks any green color in the gills which is found in *N. fasciculare*. It grows in clusters on logs and stumps of oak, chestnut, spruce and pine, from September on Clingmans Dome, and later on Mt. Mingus (November), Mt. Kephart (October), at Elkmont (November), and Cades Cove (December).

In Europe it is said to be poisonous, but the leading authorities in North America report it to be edible.

26b *Naematoloma fasciculare*

Cap ⅓ to 2 inches broad, yellow, disk buff. Odor mild, taste bitter. Gills at first pale yellow, becoming green. Stalk ¾ to 2½ inches long, concolor with the cap. Spores purplish-brown in mass.

Reports on its edibility are conflicting: some writers say it is poisonous; others report it as edible.

A typical habitat was found in Cades Cove, in October, where it grew abundantly on conifer uprooted-stumps and limbs which had been piled in an abandoned roadway. It may be sought in similar habitats. Large numbers have been found on hemlock logs on Mt. Le Conte, in Cades Cove, at Indian Creek and Elkmont, and on fir logs and fallen limbs on Clingmans Dome.

Figure 26a, about three-fourths natural size

Figure 26b, about three-fourths natural size

27

Agaricus

The genus *Agaricus* is as widely known as *Amanita* but for a very different reason. The Amanitas include some of the most poisonous of the mushrooms; the genus *Agaricus* includes the cultivated mushroom, and several other edible species. More recent studies show that some species of *Agaricus* are potentially poisonous! It is therefore advised that one would do better to purchase fresh mushrooms (canned, if preferred!) rather than risk those collected from the wild.

The spores are purple-brown, the gills are free and become dark or blackish at maturity, the stalk separates easily from the cap, and there is a ring but no volva.

Key to Agaricus Species

1. Usually on lawns, in pastures and in meadows; cap white or streaked brown; young gills bright pink . . . .
. . . .*27a, campestris*
1. Not as above 2
   2. Cap covered by soft, flat, brown or brownish-gray scales . . . .*27b, placomyces*
   2. Cap white and not conspicuously scaly; the cap and stalk becoming yellowish where bruised . . . .
. . . .*27c, sylvicola*

27a   *Agaricus campestris*

MEADOW MUSHROOM   EDIBLE

Cap 2 to 3 inches or more in breadth, white or tinged buff, smooth and silky or delicately scaly. Odor and taste pleasant. Gills at first delicate pink, becoming dull flesh, finally purple-brown. Stalk 1½ to 3 inches long, white, without a bulb. Ring white, remnants of it often cling to the margin of the cap. Spores purple-brown in mass.

The meadow mushroom not only grows wild but is the commonly cultivated mushroom grown commercially in large quantities. This species has been found at Elkmont, in an open woods, in May, but it doubtless is more common than one collection would indicate. It should be found on lawns, fields, and in meadows in the Park, as it has been found outside the Park boundary. It is highly prized for its flavor.

Figure 27a, slightly smaller than natural size

27b *Agaricus placomyces*

FLAT-CAPPED MUSHROOM   AT TIMES POISONOUS

Cap 2 to 4 inches broad, basically white but almost covered with brown, soft scales (except on the brown disk); a pink tint is characteristic of older specimens. Odor slight, taste astringent. Gills white, then pinkish, finally drab to blackish-brown. Stalk 3 to 6 inches long, tapering slightly above the bulbous base, whitish above, dingy downward. Ring ample, white, persistent. Spores smoky-brown to chocolate-brown in mass.

This *Agaricus* is edible for some persons, but apparently poisonous for others. This situation may be due to variation in the mushroom, or to variation in individual tolerance.

It is found in the Park much more frequently than the meadow mushrooms. Specimens have been collected at Indian Creek, Cosby, Greenbrier, Cataloochee, Cherokee Orchard, Elkmont, and Chimneys Camp Ground, June to October, in deciduous woods and, at times, under hemlock.

Figure 27b, about two-thirds natural size

Figure 27c, about two-thirds natural size

27c   *Agaricus sylvicola*

SYLVAN MUSHROOM   EDIBLE

Cap 2 to 3 inches broad, at first long-conic, finally convex, white with a yellow tint, center becoming yellow when rubbed, often with russet-wine-colored stains. Odor and taste mild or pleasant. Gills free, crowded, white at first then wood-brown to darker brown. Stalk 2½ to 4½ inches long, whitish above, promptly staining yellowish on bruising, with a bulb at the base. Ring median to superior, loosely attached. Spores dark-purplish.

Although this species has been found rather often elsewhere, it has been observed three times in the Park: Greenbrier in October, and on the north slope of Mt. Le Conte, on the Rainbow Falls Trail, in July and August, at 3000 feet, in dense deciduous woods.

This *Agaricus* is of excellent flavor, but every precaution must be taken against confusing it with poisonous species.

28

Stropharia

Members of this genus have a ring. The name *Stropharia*, meaning sword-belt, doubtless refers to this ring.

The spores are purple-brown, a character which, along with the ring, relates *Stropharia* to *Agaricus*. The two genera are distinct in that in *Agaricus* the gills are free, and in *Stropharia* they are attached (adnate).

Six species have been found in the Park, two of which are included here.

Key to Stropharia Species

1. Ring falling away, parts of it clinging for a time to the cap-margin; gills finally blackish . . . . *28a, coronilla*
1. Ring remaining on the stalk; gills finally drab or brownish . . . . *28b, hardii*

Figures 28a, left and above, about natural size

28a   *Stropharia coronilla*

GARLAND STROPHARIA   PROBABLY POISONOUS

Cap ¾ to 2½ inches broad, yellow to buff, margin at first fringed by veil-remnants. Odor mild, taste finally bitter. Gills white, then violet-gray, finally blackish. Stalk 1 to 2 inches long, whitish. Ring whitish, finally falling away, parts of it clinging to the cap-margin for a time. Spores blackish-brown.

This species has been found once in the Park, in mixed woods, in June. Outside the Park, it has been collected from June through October. It grows singly or more often in groups.

Its specific name, *coronilla*, may come from the fact that it often grows in handsome groups.

28b *Stropharia hardii*

EDIBILITY UNKNOWN

Cap 1 to 4 inches broad, clay-yellow, often with dark spots. Odor and taste slight or mild. Gills whitish, then mouse gray. Stalk 1½ to 3 inches long, white. Ring white, often at a mid-point or below. Spores brown in mass.

This may be the most common *Stropharia* in the Park. Collections have been taken from Greenbrier, Heintooga Overlook, Mt. Mingus, and Indian Gap, in July and August, in deciduous (often beech) woods.

Figure 28b, about two-thirds natural size

29

Coprinus (The Inky Caps)

As a group, the *Coprinus* species are popularly known as the inky caps. At maturity the hyphae of the fruiting body secrete an enzyme which dissolves the tissues, especially of the gills—an instance of auto-digestion. Although some mushrooms other than *Coprinus* exhibit this power of autodigestion, they are few in number, and in none does the enzyme seem as active or the digestion as complete as in *Coprinus*.

In addition to the interesting phenomenon of autodigestion, the *Coprini*, delicate though they may be, are able to grow under hard pavement and, by their growth-pressure, are capable of breaking through the pavement.

In the Park, there are known to date only five species of *Coprinus*, of which two are included here.

Key to Coprinus Species

1. Cap 2 to 4 inches long, shaggy with scales; growing scattered ....*29a, comatus*
1. Cap usually less than 2 inches long, with granular scales and glistening with mica-like particles; growing in clusters ....*29b, micaceus*

Figure 29a, about one-half natural size

29a   *Coprinus comatus*

SHAGGY MANE   EDIBLE

Cap more or less cylindric and 2 to 4 inches long, gradually expanding, clay color when young, the cuticle becoming torn into clay-colored scales and the white flesh showing. Taste mild. Gills soon black and dissolving to a black fluid, whence "inky caps." Stalk 2 to 4 inches or more in length, base bulbous, whitish. Ring more or less movable, thus may be found at most any point on the stalk. Spores blackish in mass.

As the caps mature they are softened by an enzyme; they are, therefore, best when eaten in the younger stages before softening.

It has not been my good fortune to find this well-known mushroom in the Park. It should be found in low, moist, open woods, and in shady pastures, from April through October. Once I found it breaking through a hard pavement on the campus of The University of Tennessee.

29b *Coprinus micaceus*

GLISTENING COPRINUS   EDIBLE

Cap ¾ to 2 inches broad, clay-brown with white, granular scales and with glistening, mica-like particles (micaceous), striate. Odor and taste slight or mild. Gills white, becoming black and deliquescing. Stalk 1 to 3 inches long, white, equal or at times slightly bulbous. Spores blackish in mass.

This small *Coprinus* grows in large clusters at the base of stumps and dead trees. Often it is found on lawns where it comes from buried wood. It has been found in May, June, and October, in Cades Cove and at Indian Gap. The glistening *Coprinus* is one of the few wild mushrooms which I have eaten. It is of fair quality.

Figures 29b, left, about one-half natural size; below, about natural size

30

Pseudocoprinus

The members of this genus have a thin, membranous, furrowed cap and black spores, and are very fragile. Although each individual in this group is small, the large numbers commonly growing in a cluster attract attention.

Figure 30a, about natural size

30a *Pseudocoprinus disseminatus*

SCATTERED MUSHROOM   EDIBLE

Cap ⅛ inch or less in breadth, whitish, then grayish-brown to grayish-pink, finally flesh-pink, white-powdery, glistening, thin, striate to disk. Gills white, then pink, finally brownish. Stalk ½ to ⅝ inches long, whitish, powdery, fragile. Spores purplish-black in mass.

This dainty mushroom grows in large numbers about stumps and buried wood, on lawns and in open woods, in August and September. It has been found at lower elevations, at the Park Headquarters, Elkmont, and in Cades Cove. Too small and thin for the mycophagist.

PART THREE
MUSHROOM RELATIVES

Key to
Common Larger Fungi

There are two choices on the left, each with the same number, 1–1, 2–2, etc. If the first choice applies to the specimen to be identified, follow the dotted line to the right of the number. If that number is 2, then proceed downward on the left to the pair of 2's, and make a choice there. This procedure should be followed until the appropriate group is reached.

The italic number preceding the name of each group refers to the order of appearance of that group in this book—i.e., Polypores (32), Boletes (33), etc. Within each group, the species are given an "a," "b," "c," etc., designation.

As noted in this key, mushrooms have gills. However, mushroom relatives, with one or two exceptions, lack gills. Some of these relatives are fleshy; others are tough, leathery, or woody.

1. Parasitic on pine limbs and causing galls which are orange-colored from spores . . . . 31, *Rusts*
1. Not producing galls on pine 2
   2. Fruiting body having a stalk and umbrella-shaped cap 3
   2. Fruiting body with a globose head or none . . 9
3. Fruiting body fleshy and bearing gills on lower surface . . . . (see pages 21–23) *Mushrooms*
3. Fruiting body without gills on lower surface . . . 4
   4. With pores or tubes on the lower surface . . . 5
   4. Not as above 7
5. Fruiting body leathery to woody . . . 32, *Polypores*

5. Fruiting body more or less fleshy 6
   6. Stalk central; cap thick-fleshy; growing on soil
     . . . . 33, *Boletes*
   6. Stalk lateral; cap thick-rubbery; growing on
     wood . . . . 34, *Fistulina*
7. Fruiting body bearing teeth on lower surface . . . 8
7. Fruiting body smooth or wrinkled . 35, *Craterellus*
   8. Cap tough-leathery to semi-fleshy . . . .
     . . . . 36, *Hydnums*
   8. Cap gelatinous-rubbery . . . .
     . . . . 36a, *Pseudohydnum gelatinosum*
9. With a stalk and head 10
9. Without a head; stalk present or absent 14
   10. Fruiting body with an offensive odor . . . .
     . . . . 37, *Stinkhorns*
   10. Odor mild 11
11. Head smooth 12
11. Head convoluted or saddle-shaped 13
   12. Head with a colored mouth; stalk gelatinous
     and spongy . . . . 38, *Calostoma*
   12. Head, internally, showing a network of cham-
     bers . . . . 39, *Pisolithus*
   12. Head without a mouth; stalk not at all gelati-
     nous; growing attached to an underground
     globose fungus . . . . . 40a, *Cordyceps capitata*
13. Head ribbed and pitted . . . . 41, *True morels*
13. Head saddle-shaped . . . . 41, *False morels*
   14. Fruiting body erect, branched or un-
     branched 15
   14. Not as above 22
15. Fruiting body with branches, at times repeatedly
   branched 16
15. Fruiting body unbranched, at least not re-
   peatedly branched 18
   16. Fruiting body fleshy, white or colored (often
     buff) . . . . 42, *Coral fungi*
   16. Fruiting body leathery and tough 17
17. Branches distinct and separate but forked, the tips
   acute . . . . 42b, *Thelephora palmata*

17. Branches more or less fused downward, the tips blunt . . . .*42f, Tremellodendron pallidum*
   18. Fruiting body tough, leathery, or hard 20
   18. Fruiting body fleshy or gelatinous 19
19. Fruiting body a gelatinous head [not illustrated] . . . .*Jew's-ear and relatives*
19. Fruiting body fleshy 21
   20. Fruiting body a convoluted, more or less globose head; no stalk . . .*42e, Sparassis crispa*
   20. Fruiting body erect, blackish, slender . . . .*43, Xylaria (Dead-man's-fingers)*
21. Parasitic on and growing from buried insects or subterranean fungi . . . .*40, Cordyceps*
21. Growing from soil . . . .*44, Earthtongues*
   22. Fruiting body more or less cup-shaped 23
   22. Fruiting body not cup-shaped 24
23. Cup more or less leathery, containing egglike bodies . . . .*45, Bird's-nest fungi*
23. Cup fleshy, no "eggs" . . . .*46, Cup fungi*
   24. Fruiting body at least at first more or less globose to pear-shaped; the outer wall splitting in a star-shaped fashion . . . . . .*47, Earthstars*
   24. Fruiting body wall not splitting; interior at first white and soft, finally transformed into a mass of powdery spores . . . . . .*48, Puffballs*

31

Rusts

From ancient times, farmers, naturalists, and others have observed and discussed the rusts. Some rusts attack farm crops and bring about considerable destruction. Rusts are members of the fungus kingdom, and are somewhat distantly related to mushrooms, but are parasitic on higher plants. Rusts, of course, are not eaten. Within the Park, eighty-four species have been found. Some live their whole cycle on one higher plant (the host). Other species require two different, rather distantly related host-plants, such as pine—sunflower; pine—coreopsis; pine—aster or goldenrod; red cedar—service-berry or hawthorn; balsam (fir)—fern; bluet—blue-eyed grass; hemlock—hydrangea.

One of the more conspicuous species of rusts in the Park is *Cronartium quercuum*, the oak-pine rust.

31a *Cronartium quercuum*

OAK-PINE RUST

Typical of many rust fungi, this species lives a portion of its cycle on one plant (in this instance, on living pine), and the balance of its cycle on an unrelated plant (here on living oak leaves). It is not only able to live on oak and pine, but is also obliged to live on these two kinds of trees. If either oak or pine is absent from the area, the rust does not develop.

It has been found, in April, on pine trunks and limbs, especially scrub pine and yellow pine, where it is a parasite. There it stimulates the bark tissues to enlarge and thus to cause galls. When the rust fungus is mature, numerous blisters appear on the gall. The thin cover on each blister is white, and when broken exposes the orange-colored spore-mass.

At maturity, in May and June, these spores developed on pine are carried by the wind to living oak leaves where they bring about rust-infection. On oak leaves the rust appears as brown, minute horns. The oak species infected by the rust in the Park include: white oak (*Quercus alba*), shingle oak (*Q. imbricaria*), northern red oak (*Q. rubra*), and black oak (*Q. velutina*). Probably all oaks in the Park are susceptible to this rust.

Figure 31a, about three-fourths natural size

32

Polypores (Brackets and Conks)

This group of fungi is represented in the Park by a large number of conspicuous species. They have tubes on the lower side of the cap, much as in the boletes, but all are either woody or leathery, or at times slightly fleshy, in contrast to the soft, fleshy texture of the boletes. Because they are tough, nearly all of the polypores are inedible.

All polypores have a cap, and some have a central or lateral stalk; others have no stalk at all, in which instances their caps are laterally attached to the substratum.

They grow on living tree trunks, logs, fallen limbs, stumps, lumber, and may cause decay of structural timbers, or buried wood.

Some polypores have been used in the manufacture of tinder. In days gone by, others of this group constituted a source of medicine for many human disorders. One, *Fomes officinalis*, is still on the list of sources of certain medicines—one in particular, a purgative; another, as a substitute for quinine. This species has not been found in the Park.

There are more than one hundred species known in the Park, of which eleven are included in the key.

Key to the Polypores

1. The polypore growing in a cluster of many caps 2
1. The polypore growing singly, not in a cluster 3
    2. Caps yellowish, often sulphur yellow, each cap much more than 1 inch broad . . . .
    . . . . .32*a, Polyporus sulphureus*

2. Caps whitish to smoky, each cap 1 inch or less broad .... 32b, *Polyporus umbellatus*

3. Cap with a central or sub-central stalk 4

3. Cap without a stalk, or if present the stalk is composed of a lateral prolongation of the cap 6

4. Cap relatively small (1½ to 3 inches broad), scaly, leathery; pores conspicuous and angular .... 32c, *Polyporus arcularius*

4. Cap larger (2 to 8 inches broad), not scaly; pores small 5

5. Cap fleshy-tough; stalk with a long, black "root" ... . 32d, *Polyporus radicatus*

5. Cap sub-fleshy, often two or more caps fused at their edges; stalk pallid and not rooting .... 32e, *Polyporus cristatus*

6. Cap with its lower surface bearing gill-like structures rather than pores 7

6. Cap with typical pores 8

7. Gills, if present, also accompanied by pores .... 32f, *Daedalea confragosa*

7. Gills distinct; cap zoned and hairy .... 32g, *Lenzites betulina*

8. Cap large (up to 6 or more inches broad), thick, woody, interior showing a layer for each year of growth; on conifers .... 32h, *Fomes pinicola*

8. Cap smaller, or if large then shining and mahogany-colored, not showing annual growth-layers, not hard and woody 9

9. Cap up to 6 or 8 inches broad, corky, shining, mahogany-colored; stalk, if present, laterally attached .... 32i, *Polyporus tsugae*

9. Not as above 10

10. Cap-zones of many colors (brown, red, yellow, blue, or even whitish) ... 32j, *Polyporus versicolor*

10. Cap-zones of one color, or if many-colored not conspicuously so 11

11. Pore-surface whitish to brownish, usually tinged violaceous; on conifers ...... 32k, *Polyporus abietinus*

11. Pore-surface brownish, no violet tints, pores round or elongated to irregular and meandering; on deciduous-tree wood .... 32f, *Daedalea confragosa*

32a *Polyporus sulphureus*

SULPHUR POLYPORE   EDIBLE

Caps in large clusters, more or less rosette-like, the cluster 8 to 20 inches or more broad, fleshy-firm when fresh, color some shade of yellow—sulphur yellow, pale yellow—fading in age to whitish. Flesh white to yellowish. Pore-surface sulphur yellow, fading. Stalk none, but at times with a stalklike base.

When young and tender, the sulphur polypore is good eating. It grows on logs or other wood of both coniferous and deciduous trees, at all elevations in the Park. It has been found at Newfound Gap, Elkmont, atop Mt. Le Conte, Greenbrier, and on Hannah Mountain, from June through August.

Figure 32a, about one-fourth natural size
(from collection of Dr. L. O. Overholts)

Figure 32b, about one-half natural size
(photograph courtesy of Dr. S. A. Cain)

32b *Polyporus umbellatus*

UMBELLATE OR MANY-CAPPED POLYPORE   EDIBLE

Caps numerous and small, forming a large cluster—
the clusters 3 to 6 inches broad, each depressed in the center, whitish or smoky, thin. Flesh white. Tubes whitish, extending down the stalk, small. Stalk whitish, branched,
the branches cylindric, frequently attached to a buried
sclerotium.

This clustered polypore occurs on soil, in deciduous
woods, from May through August, at Indian Creek, in
Greenbrier, and near Gatlinburg.

32c *Polyporus arcularius*

ANGULAR-PORED POLYPORE   EDIBLE, BUT TOUGH

Cap ½ to 3 inches broad, center depressed, yellowish-brown to dark brown, tough-leathery, scaly, the margin sometimes hairy. Flesh white, thin. Pores angular, surface white to yellowish, tubes $\frac{1}{10}$ of an inch or less in length. Stalk central, ½ to 2½ inches long, yellowish-brown or dark brown, at times scaly.

This polypore grows on dead wood, at times on buried wood, of deciduous trees scattered over the Park. It has been found from April through June, in Greenbrier, at Park Headquarters, and on Rich Mountain.

Figure 32c, about natural size

32d *Polyporus radicatus*

ROOTING POLYPORE   EDIBILITY UNKNOWN

Cap 1 to 8 inches broad, fleshy-tough, yellowish-brown or smoky-brown, velvety or scurfy. Flesh white, rather thin. Pore-surface white or yellowish. Stalk 2 to 5 inches long, dingy above, with a long black root which is usually attached to buried wood.

This is as striking as it is uncommon. To date, it has not been found in the Park, but its occurrence in East Tennessee and North Carolina, and elsewhere in the eastern half of the United States, suggests that the rooting polypore should be found in the Park. It is tough and would scarcely be palatable.

Figure 32d, about three-fourths natural size

Figure 32e, about two-thirds natural size

32e   *Polyporus cristatus*

CRESTED POLYPORE   EDIBLE

Cap 2 to 6 or 8 inches broad, fleshy to sub-fleshy, yellowish-green, yellowish-brown, or tan, often becoming cracked at maturity. Flesh white. Pore-surface white to yellowish or green. Stalk 1 to 2½ inches long, pallid to whitish.

At times the caps fuse at their margins into a mass of three or more fruiting bodies. It has been found in Cades Cove, at Indian Creek, and at Indian Camp Creek, all in August. It grows in the vicinity of oak, chestnut, and other deciduous trees.

When sliced and stewed, it is said to be of good flavor.

32f *Daedalea confragosa*

WILLOW OR ROUGH POLYPORE   UNPALATABLE, TOUGH

Cap 1 to 4 inches broad, leathery or slightly woody, zoned, grayish, smoky, or brownish. Pore-surface whitish to wood-brown, at times staining pinkish where bruised. Pores may be circular (tubelike), or irregular in shape to meandering, occasionally gill-like. Stalk none; cap attached laterally.

This polypore is interesting because of the extreme variability of the pore-surface: this surface may be composed of pores, or winding to meandering chambers (pores), or gills. It grows generally over the Park, having been collected at Tremont, Cades Cove, Alum Cave Parking Area, and on Forrester Ridge, in August and September. It is found on various deciduous trees, especially on fallen limbs of willow, dogwood, and birch.

It causes a white decay of sapwood.

Figure 32f, about three-fourths natural size

Figure 32g, about three-fourths natural size

Figure 32h, about three-fourths natural size

32g *Lenzites betulina*

BIRCH POLYPORE   UNPALATABLE, LEATHERY

Cap 1 to 4 inches broad, leathery to corky, attached laterally, grayish to brownish, zoned, more or less hairy. Flesh white. Gills present similar to those of mushrooms, no pores. Stalk none.

The name *betulina* is derived from its frequent growth on birch. The name *Lenzites* was first assigned to this polypore in honor of Lenz, a German botanist. It is widespread and common in the Park, having been collected at Greenbrier, Cherokee Orchard, and Tremont, on oak and other deciduous trees and logs, throughout the year.

The birch polypore is said to cause decay of the sapwood.

32h *Fomes pinicola*

PINE-INHABITING POLYPORE   UNPALATABLE, WOODY

Cap 4 to 6 or more inches broad, color varying from blackish, brown, or reddish-brown to grayish, hard and woody. Flesh pale or wood-colored, at times pale yellow, turning pinkish where wounded. Pore-surface whitish to smoky, rarely pale-yellowish. Stalk none.

Although this polypore may be found on oak, beech, and other deciduous trees, it grows most commonly in the Park on conifers. It has been found on standing trees and logs of hemlock, spruce, and fir at numerous stations including: Boulevard Trail, Spruce Flats, Clingmans Dome, Sugarland Mountain, and others. Because of its woody texture it persists through the year. The *Fomes* group all are perennial and add a layer of growth year after year. A cut through the cap shows a layer for each year of its age.

It causes a brown decay of both sapwood and heartwood of dead trees, chiefly of conifers.

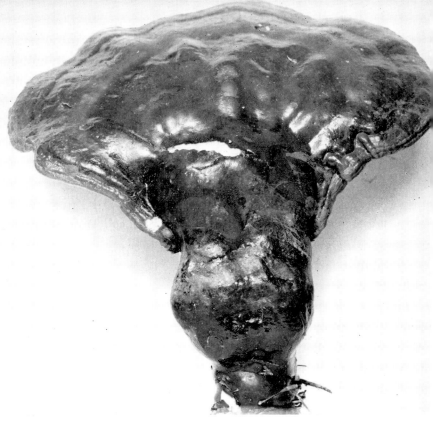

Figure 32i, about three-fourths natural size

32i *Polyporus tsugae*

HEMLOCK POLYPORE   UNPALATABLE, TOUGH

Cap 2 to 8 inches or more broad, soft-corky, mahogany-brown or blackish, shining. Flesh whitish. Pore-surface white to brownish, discolored when bruised. Stalk absent, or when present more or less laterally attached, colored like the cap.

This striking fungus has been found almost always on logs, stumps, and standing, dead trunks of hemlock. It has been collected on Mt. Le Conte, at Alum Cave Parking Area, Greenbrier, and Bear Pen Hollow, from June through August and later. Once it was found on pine in Cades Cove. The caps persist on the substratum through the winter, although in age they tend to become moldy.

The hemlock polypore produces a decay of the wood.

32j *Polyporus versicolor*

MANY-COLORED POLYPORE   UNPALATABLE

Cap ½ to 2 inches broad, with zones of many colors (whitish, yellow, brown, red, blue), leathery, more or less velvety. Flesh thin, white. Pore-surface white or yellowish. Stalk none; cap laterally attached.

The many-colored polypore causes a rot of the sapwood of dead trees, logs, and limbs. It disintegrates the woody substance so that it reduces the weight of an affected limb. One of the most common of conspicuous fungi in the Park, it has been collected on birch, oak, chestnut, and other deciduous dead-woody parts, from July through the autumn, at many stations (Mt. Le Conte, Cades Cove, Roaring Fork, and others).

Figure 32j, about natural size

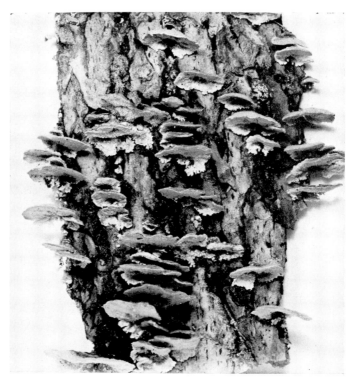

Figure 32k, about two-thirds natural size

32k *Polyporus abietinus*

FIR POLYPORE   UNPALATABLE, TOUGH

Cap ⅓ to 1⅔ inches broad, somewhat leathery, attached laterally and shelving, white, gray, or smoky, somewhat hairy, more or less zonate. Flesh white to grayish, thin ($\frac{1}{25}$ of an inch or less). Pore-surface white to brownish, often with a violet tint, tubes often splitting. Stalk none.

This species is common, often abundant, and almost world-wide. It has been collected on pine in Cades Cove, and on fir atop Clingmans Dome, Mt. Kephart, and Mt. Le Conte, from July through September, and may be seen in the Park on almost any walk through coniferous woods.

It is too tough to be considered for eating.

33

Boletes

The group known as boletes generally resemble mushrooms in that they are fleshy, and have a cap and stalk. They differ in that they have tubes (pores) instead of gills on the lower side of the cap. Whether or not they should be called mushrooms depends on one's definition of a mushroom. Most of them are edible, and the layman may consider them to be mushrooms.

Most naturalists, whether amateur or professional, have some acquaintance with the genus *Boletus*. But, there are, in addition, two other closely related genera, namely *Boletinus* and *Strobilomyces*. Representatives of all three genera are found in the Park. Distinctions among the three are as follows: (1) in *Boletus*, the pores (tubes) are easily separable from the cap-flesh; (2) in *Boletinus* the tubes are not easily separable from the cap-flesh; (3) in *Strobilomyces*, generally similar to *Boletinus*, the cap and stalk show conspicuous, soft warts and scales.

References to *Boleti* have been made in literature from ancient days. The Romans lacked the understanding of boletes which we have today, but these plants had a place in the lives of those early people. The Romans recommended the use of certain boletes (as lotions and salves) for various human ailments including rheumatism, sore eyes, dog bites, skin ulcers, and for the removal of freckles and blemishes from the faces of the fairer sex.

The cap in one species may be dry; in another

species, viscid or glutinous. Colors vary with the species. The cap-flesh may be whitish or yellow, and oddly enough, depending on the species, may change color when broken, cut, or bruised. The changed color may be blue, pink, or brownish. Likewise, the tubes, according to the species, may also change color where bruised. The bruised stalk may or may not show this capacity to change color. Stalks may exhibit a network on their surfaces. A few species have a veil which later forms a ring, or annulus, on the stalk.

Boletes grow on the soil, more rarely on decaying logs, in deciduous and coniferous woods. A majority perhaps form mycorrhiza with forest trees; for example, *Boletus luteus* not only grows under or near pine trees but also forms a mycorrhizal relationship with the roots of pine. Boletes are said to be eaten by bears and cattle, and, in the winter, reindeer dig them out of the snow as forage.

In the Park, there are about eighty species of *Boleti* of which fourteen are included in the key. One of these is a parasite on a type of puffball.

Key to the Boletes

1. Growing as a parasite on a puffball . . . .
. . . . 33*a, Boletus parasiticus*
1. Not growing as a parasite 2
   2. Ring present on the upper portion of the stalk. . .3
   2. Ring absent 5
3. Ring and cap glutinous, or slimy . .33*b, Boletus luteus*
3. Ring and cap dry or only slightly viscid 4
   4. Cap and stalk with dense, dark, soft warts or scales; tube-mouths in age becoming black . . . .
. . . . .33*c, Strobilomyces floccopus*
   4. Cap and stalk scaly, the scales bright or dark red; tube-mouths yellow, in age becoming light brown
. . . . .33*d, Boletinus pictus*
5. Cap slimy, brown; stalk relatively short (usually ½ to 1½ inches long); tubes and stalk at first white . . . . .
. . . . .33*e, Boletus brevipes*

5. Not with the above combination of characters 6
   6. Cap dark brown or olive-tan, with numerous white or yellowish spots . . . .
   . . . . *33f, Boletus affinis* var. *maculosus*
   6. Cap not spotted 7
7. Mouths of tubes red, becoming bluish where bruised; cap brown or red with olive streaks and areas . . . .
   . . . . 33g, *Boletus luridus*
7. Tube-mouths not red 8
   8. Flesh of cap when cut, broken, or bruised, changing in color 9
   8. Flesh of cap unchanging 11
9. Stalk with a prominent reticulation especially on upper half; cap grayish; cap-flesh grayish or white, becoming pink or brown when cut . . . . 33h, *Boletus griseus*
9. Stalk not reticulated 10
   10. Stalk with numerous reddish or brownish dots (squamules) 11
   10. Stalk absent of such dots 12
11. Cap-flesh yellowish, becoming pinkish-brown when cut; cap yellow, tinged or spotted red; dots on stalk viscid . . . . 33i, *Boletus americanus*
11. Cap-flesh yellowish, becoming reddish when cut; cap with red, olive, and gold tints; dots on stalk not viscid . . . . 33j, *Boletus morrisii*
   12. Cap yellow or chamois; cap-flesh yellowish, becoming pale blue when cut . . . .
   . . . . 33k, *Boletus melleoluteus*
   12. Cap rosy or purplish-red; tubes becoming gray-blue or blue where bruised . . 33l, *Boletus bicolor*
   12. Cap and tubes not as above 13
13. Stalk with a network of prominent ridges . . . .
   . . . . 33m, *Boletus russellii*
13. Stalk with numerous reddish dots 14
   14. Cap yellowish, densely covered with fibrillose, erect tufts (scales); cap-flesh staining paper a gray-green color; odor fragrant . . . .
   . . . . 33n, *Boletus hirtellus*
   14. Cap yellow, tinged or spotted red, without tufts (scales); odor sour (acidulous) . . . .
   . . . . 33i, *Boletus americanus*

Figure 33a, about three-fourths natural size

33a   *Boletus parasiticus*

PARASITIC BOLETE   EDIBLE, POOR QUALITY

Cap 1 to 2½ inches broad, surface dry, rather leathery, becoming cracked, yellowish-brown to olivaceous, or grayish-yellow. Flesh white, becoming yellow when cut. Pore-surface yellow, finally olivaceous, not changing color where bruised. Stalk 1 to 2 inches long, color similar to the cap, with numerous dark flecks. Spores blackish-olive.

This is an interesting find. Its parasitic mode of life—living on the puffball *Scleroderma aurantium*—distinguishes it from other boletes. It has been found along the Rainbow Falls Trail on Mt. Le Conte, at Meigs Creek, and at Indian Creek, in July and August.

33b *Boletus luteus*

Cap 1 to 3½ inches broad, slimy, brownish to reddish-yellow or dark tan, mottled and streaked with darker lines and patches. Flesh pale yellow, tinged flesh, unchanging. Odor slight, taste faintly sour. Tubes pale yellow, finally dull clay, unchanging when bruised, mouths dotted with sticky particles. Stalk 2 to 3 inches long, yellow or darker above, whitish below, dotted and splotched with dark gluten. Ring consisting of a glutinous membrane. Spores golden brown or olive-green.

This species is found in pine woods or, less commonly, in mixed woods, from August through October. Thus far I have it in the collection from Cades Cove only, but I have seen it from other areas of the Park.

It is said to be excellent eating. The stalk and the slime should be removed before cooking.

Figure 33b, about seven-eighths natural size

33c *Strobilomyces floccopus*

CONE-LIKE BOLETE   EDIBLE

Cap 2½ to 5 inches broad, dry, densely covered with large, dark, soft, cottony warts and scales, the color between the scales paler or whitish, the margin bearing veil-fragments. Flesh white, when cut changing to red then blackish. Odor and taste mild. Tubes at first white, at maturity dark to blackish. Stalk 2½ to 4 inches long, more or less scaly like the cap, with a soft ring left by the veil. Spores black in mass.

This has been collected on the north slope of Mt. Le Conte, at 2500 feet, along the Rainbow Falls Trail, and observed at many other stations. After rains, in July through September, it may be expected on almost any walk through the woods. Another closely related species, *Strobilomyces confusus*, also grows in the Park. This latter species is found more rarely, and has been seen at Spruce Flats, in September.

Figure 33c, about two-thirds natural size

Figure 33d, about three-fourths natural size

33d *Boletinus pictus*

PAINTED BOLETE   EDIBLE

Cap 1 to 4½ inches broad, dry or slightly viscid, when fresh bright to dark red, often yellowish toward the margin, fading in age, squamulose. Flesh creamy-yellow, slowly becoming reddish when cut or bruised. Tubes yellow when fresh, later light brown, not changing color when bruised. Stalk 1½ to 3 inches long, colored like the cap. Veil whitish, leaving for a time a soft roll at the stalk-apex. Spores yellowish-brown.

This beautiful species is commonly found in the Park, although I have it only from Cades Cove and Rich Mountain, June through September. It may be expected in coniferous, especially pine, and mixed woods.

Figure 33e, about natural size

33e *Boletus brevipes*

SHORT-STALKED BOLETE   EDIBLE

Cap 1½ to 4 inches broad, brownish to reddish-chest-nut, with dark stains, glutinous. Flesh white or yellowish, not changing color where bruised. Odor and taste mild. Tubes adnate-decurrent, white then yellowish, not changing color. Stalk ½ to 1½ inches long, tapering downward, white then yellow with brown stains, moist, scarcely viscid. Spores cinnamon-buff.

After rains in the autumn, this should be found in any pine woods in the Park. It has been collected in pine woods near the Park Headquarters, and in Cades Cove, from September through November. At lower elevations and farther south, it fruits in December and January—a winter species.

Figure 33f, about natural size

33f   *Boletus affinis* var. *maculosus*

SPOTTED BOLETE   EDIBLE

Cap 2 to 3½ inches broad, dry, olive-tan to dark brown, with white spots. Flesh of cap white, unchanging when cut. Tubes at first white or pale flesh-colored, in age becoming sordid yellowish-buff, turning yellow or brownish where bruised, at times depressed around the stalk. Stalk 1½ to 3 inches long, base tapering, tan or brown. Spores yellowish with a faint olive tint.

Although there are, in The University of Tennessee Herbarium, only two collections from the Park, it is rather frequently seen there. It has been found at Newfound Gap in September, and at Alum Cave Parking Area in August, under rhododendron.

The caps are good eating; the stalks, although edible, fail to cook well.

Figure 33g, about three-fifths natural size

33g *Boletus luridus*

LURID BOLETEPOISONOUS

Cap 2 to 5 inches broad or larger, slightly viscid, brownish to reddish, with blackish or olivaceous streaks and areas. Flesh thick, whitish or pale yellow, turning blue when cut. Odor acid, taste mild and pleasant. Tubes red, fading at maturity, greenish-yellowish inside, greenish-blue when cut or bruised, small and compact. Stalk 2 to 4 inches long, bulky, apex yellow, elsewhere like the cap, flesh of stalk quickly blue on wounding. Spores olive-smoky.

This is a large bolete, at times 6 to 8 inches broad. It has been found in deciduous and mixed woods, near Cherokee Orchard, Spruce Flats, and Greenbrier, from June through August.

It is said to have a pleasing taste but is reputed to be poisonous.

33h *Boletus griseus*

Cap 3 to 6 inches broad, dry, light gray to dark gray, rather thick. Flesh gray-white or dull yellow, becoming pinkish on long exposure when cut. Odor a delicate fruit fragrance, taste slightly sweet. Tubes whitish then grayish to clay, brown where bruised, adnate and depressed. Stalk 2 to 4½ inches long, whitish to yellowish, with conspicuous, darker reticulations, base often crooked. Spores dull clay-brown.

Mostly this bolete is found in deciduous woods, but at times in mixed woods. It has been found in Cades Cove, on the north slope of Mt. Le Conte, and at Cosby, from July through September.

Figure 33h, about three-fifths natural size

331 *Boletus americanus*

Cap 1½ to 4 inches broad, chrome yellow, tinged or spotted reddish, viscid, margin at first with reddish fragments. Flesh yellowish, turning pinkish-brown then yellow when cut. Odor slightly sour, taste of flesh mild (but the cuticle acid). Tubes dull-yellowish then brownish, adnate or decurrent, often in radial rows. Stalk 1 to 2 inches long, yellow, with reddish-brown, viscid glandular dots. No veil present. Spores rusty-yellowish.

After late summer and autumn rains, one is certain to find boletes in pine woods. A common one is *B. americanus*. It has been recorded from Newfound Gap in August, and Cades Cove from August through November.

Figure 331, about five-sixths natural size

33j *Boletus morrisii*

MORRIS BOLETE   EDIBILITY UNKNOWN

Cap 2 to 4 inches broad, dark olive or greenish in youth, finally reddish-brown or olive-brown with an olive-gold margin. Flesh light yellow, changing slowly to reddish when cut. Odor and taste none. Tubes clear yellow or at times brownish-red toward the stalk, red when bruised. Stalk 2 to 3 inches long, greenish-yellow, with numerous red dots. Spores olive.

This bolete has been found in August and September, on the north slope of Mt. Le Conte, at Indian Creek and in Cades Cove, in mixed and pine woods, at times under rhododendron.

Its edibility appears not to have been tested.

Figure 33j, about five-sixths natural size

33k   *Boletus melleoluteus*

Cap 1 to 3 inches broad, honey-yellow, chamois, or brighter yellow, dry. Flesh yellow, blue when cut (at times slowly and slightly blue). Odor and taste mild. Tubes whitish to pale yellow, finally deep sea-foam green, darker greenish when bruised, slightly depressed around the stalk. Stalk 1 to 2½ inches long, colored like the cap, base curved, apex white, yellowish below. Spores light brownish-olive.

This species is rather new to science. It was first found on September 6, 1947, near the picnic area in Cades Cove in mixed woods. A description of it was published in the journal, *Mycologia*, volume 43, in 1951. Since the first collection was made, it has been found in Cades Cove, near the Park Headquarters, at Indian Creek, and outside the Park at Highlands, North Carolina, in August and September.

Its edibility has not been tested.

Figure 33k, about three-fourths natural size

Figure 33l, about one-half natural size

33l   *Boletus bicolor*

TWO-COLOR BOLETE   EDIBLE

Cap 2 to 6 inches broad, dry, dark red (rosy or purplish), fading and becoming yellowish-mottled. Flesh thick, yellow, becoming golden yellow on exposure. Odor and taste mild. Tubes yellow, finally olive or brownish, becoming blue to greenish-blue where wounded, adnate-depressed around the stalk. Stalk 2½ to 4 inches long, yellow at the apex, red below, becoming blue when wounded. Spores olive.

This handsome two-color, red and yellow, bolete is not difficult to find and identify. It has been collected at Indian Creek in August, Cherokee Orchard from July through September, Greenbrier in July, and White Oak Sinks in August. It may be looked for in mixed woods, often on the banks of road-cuts near woods.

Figure 33m, about two-thirds natural size

33m *Boletus russellii*

RUSSELL BOLETE   EDIBLE

Cap 1 to 2 inches broad, dry, with tiny, erect fiber-clusters, brownish-yellow. Flesh yellow, unchanging. Tubes cream-colored, finally greenish-yellow, unchanging. Stalk 3 to 4 inches long, tapering upward, base curved, strongly netted with platelike ridges, flesh-colored or red. Spores dark brown with an olive tint.

This bolete has been found in August and September in Cades Cove, in deciduous woods. It is rather rare but is included because of its striking netted and ridged stalk.

It is said to be soft and of good flavor when cooked. McIlvaine suggests that the tubes and stalk should be discarded and only the cap-flesh eaten.

33n *Boletus hirtellus*

Cap 1 to 3 inches broad, viscid, orange, buff, or yellow, with dense tufts of fibrils. Flesh pale yellow, unchanging but staining paper greenish-yellow. Odor fragrant when fresh, taste none. Tubes pale yellow, finally brownish, unchanging where bruised. Stalk 1½ to 2½ inches long, yellowish, base often crooked, reddish-dotted more or less all over, expanding below into plates of mycelium. Spores olive-brown.

This species is fairly common despite the single collection I have from the Park. It was found on the north slope of Mt. Le Conte, at 3000 feet, in August, in pine woods.

Figure 33n, about three-fourths natural size

34

Fistulina

Two species of this genus are known from the Park. One is rare, and the other (*F. hepatica*) is common and conspicuous. The latter is popular with those who are at home in the woods because of its attractive colors, shelving habit, and edibility.

34a *Fistulina hepatica*

BEEFSTEAK FUNGUS   EDIBLE

Cap 4 to 8 inches broad, dark red to reddish-brown, or liver-colored, fleshy, the texture and color suggesting beefsteak, attached laterally. Flesh reddish, taste slightly acid. Pore-surface yellowish or slightly pink, finally dingy; the tubes stand free from one another. Stalk absent; or, if present, very short, and lateral.

The beefsteak fungus is well-known to mycophagists. Because of its pores (tubes), it is closely related to the polypores and boletes.

One is rather certain to find the beefsteak fungus each year, July through October. It grows on deciduous trees, logs, and stumps, and has been found at Cosby, Mt. Le Conte, Gregory Bald, and Cades Cove. A close relative, *Fistulina pallida*, grows at Indian Creek.

Figure 34a, about two-thirds natural size

35

Craterellus

The name *Craterellus* refers to crater, or bowl—
suggested by the shape of the cap. In the Park, five
species have been found in addition to one or two
awaiting identification.

The species in this group grow on humus and
soil, in damp woods, often in groups of several fruiting
bodies.

Two of the most common and conspicuous
species are included here. Since one is yellow and the
other is blackish, a key seems unnecessary.

Figure 35a, about three-fourths natural size

35a *Craterellus cantharellus*

FALSE CHANTEREL EDIBLE

Cap 1 to 3 inches broad, yellow, at times apricot-tinted, convex becoming depressed or funnel-shaped, fleshy (soft like a mushroom), margin more or less lobed. Smooth or more often radiately wrinkled, or ridged, on the yellow, lower surface of the cap. Stalk ½ to 2 inches long, colored like the cap.

This species resembles in shape and color *Cantharellus cibarius*, but that species has gills. In *Craterellus* radiating ridges take the place of gills.

Craterellus cantharellus is said to be of excellent flavor. It has been seen at many stations in the Park, including Rich Mountain and Cades Cove, under oak and pine, in June, July, and August.

35b *Craterellus cornucopioides*

TRUMPET CRATERELLUS   EDIBLE

Cap 1 to 2½ inches broad, very thin, smoky-brown to black, becoming deeply depressed or funnel-shaped, margin wavy and lobed. The lower surface of the cap is smoky, wrinkled or smooth. Stalk 1 to 2 inches long, or at times very short, smoky-brown, hollow.

The blackish, trumpet-shaped, or cornucopia-shaped cap characterizes this species. It often grows in clusters, nearly always in large groups, and rarely singly. It is said to be of good flavor.

Figure 35b, about three-fourths natural size

36

Hydnums (Hedgehog Fungi)

All hydnums, whatever their botanical name, have awl-shaped spines on the lower surface of the cap. Most of them have a stalk and cap, as in the mushrooms, but some species are branched, and still other forms may be found. Some are quite fleshy, others are leathery to somewhat woody. One species included here, *Pseudohydnum gelatinosum*, is watery to rubbery-gelatinous.

Of the forty-one species of hydnums in the Park, six are included here.

Key to the Hydnums

1. Fruiting body pallid, watery to rubbery-gelatinous; attached laterally, growing on logs ....36a, *Pseudohydnum gelatinosum*
1. Fruiting body not as above, either fleshy, leathery, to more or less woody 2
    2. Fruiting body whitish, extensively branched, the ultimate branches small; spines on the lower surface of the branches ....36b, *Hericium laciniatum*
    2. Fruiting body not branched, but composed of a cap and stalk 3
3. Fruiting body fleshy; cap buff or tan ....36c, *Hydnum repandum*
3. Fruiting body leathery at maturity 4
    4. Odor mild; cap becoming perforated into the stalk ....36d, *Sarcodon imbricatus*
    4. Odor of new meal 5
5. Cap hairy-fibrillose, yellowish to buff-brown; taste of meal becoming peppery ....36e, *Sarcodon cristatus*
5. Cap not hairy, becoming cracked and scaly, brownish; taste very bitter ....36f, *Sarcodon fennicus*

Figure 36a, about three-fourths natural size

36a *Pseudohydnum gelatinosum*

GELATINOUS FALSE-HYDNUM   EDIBLE

Cap 1 to 2½ inches broad, watery-rubbery-gelatinous, whitish, pallid, or grayish, laterally attached. Spines or teeth whitish or grayish, straight, more or less gelatinous. Stalk none; cap usually contracted behind to form a stalk-like elongation. Spores white.

Because of its texture this species is not regarded as a true *Hydnum*. It is placed with the hydnums here because its teeth would suggest a relationship.

Although common, only five collections have been taken in the Park—at Indian Gap, Elkmont, and Cades Cove. It grows on logs of hemlock, spruce, and pine, from July through November.

36b *Hericium laciniatum*

BRANCHED, OR LOBED, HYDNUM   EDIBLE

Fruiting body 3 to 6 inches broad, extensively branched, the ultimate branches small and delicate, white, becoming yellowish or brownish in age. Spines or teeth mostly on the lower surface of the branches, but some on sides near the ends. Odor and taste slight. Spores white.

This strikingly beautiful *Hydnum* is not seen every year. I have three collections from the Park: Greenbrier in September, Indian Gap in September, and the Gregory Bald Trail in June. It grows on logs of beech and chestnut, and doubtless on oak and logs of other deciduous trees.

Figure 36b, about natural size

36c *Hydnum repandum*

Cap 1½ to 4 inches broad, tan, cream-colored, or buff, at times orange-tinted. Odor mild, taste mild or slightly acrid. Spines on lower side of cap, pale-yellowish or white. Stalk 1½ to 3 inches long, whitish or buff, usually paler than the cap. Spores white.

This *Hydnum* also bears the common names of up-turned-cap *Hydnum*, spreading *Hydnum*, and toothed fungus.

Usually this species grows scattered or singly, rarely in groups sufficient for a large meal. Mycologists who have eaten it say that it has good flavor.

It has been found in Cades Cove and Rich Mountain to Cataloochee on the east and Indian Creek on the south of the Park. It will be found from June to December, in deciduous and coniferous woods.

Figure 36c, about natural size

36d *Sarcodon imbricatus*

TILE HYDNUM   EDIBLE

Cap 2 to 6 or 8 inches broad, at first light brown then darker brown, center depressed, in age perforated into the stalk, scaly. Odor none, but aromatic when drying, taste mildly bitter (less bitter than *S. fennicus*). Spines at first pale gray-brown, then darker brown. Stalk light brown then darker. Spores buff-brown.

This species is doubtless more widespread in the Park than my two collections suggest. It was found in Cades Cove in July and September, in deciduous woods.

Some mycophagists report it of excellent flavor, others say it has little flavor. The common name, tile *Hydnum*, is suggested by the fact that the scales on the cap may overlap.

Figure 36d, about two-thirds natural size

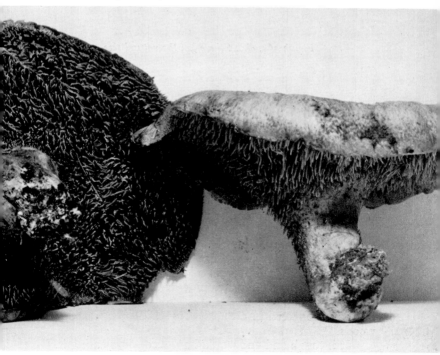

Figure 36e, about three-fourths natural size

36e   *Sarcodon cristatus*

CRESTED HYDNUM   EDIBILITY UNKNOWN

Cap 1 to 4 inches broad, at times larger, soon densely hairy, yellowish to straw-color or buff-brown. Odor of new meal, taste of new meal and becoming peppery. Spines brownish-straw, soon darker with pale tips. Stalk 1 to 2½ inches long, colored like the cap. Spores brown with a wine tint.

This species has been found in Cades Cove only. Further search will doubtless reveal its presence elsewhere in the Park. It grows in either pine or deciduous woods, in August and September. At Highlands, North Carolina, it has been collected in a huckleberry thicket, in deciduous woods.

It is tough and one would hardly consider eating it.

36f *Sarcodon fennicus*

FINNISH HYDNUM   UNPALATABLE, BITTER

Cap 2 to 5 inches broad, becoming cracked and more or less scaly, brownish, at times tinged reddish or purplish. Odor of meal, taste of meal and bitter. Spines fawn-colored to brown, tips white. Stalk 1½ to 3 inches long, colored like the cap, the base blue-green or dark olive. Spores fawn-brown in mass.

This *Hydnum* may be expected on soil, in deciduous woods almost everywhere in the Park, from June through October. It is most abundant in August. Stations where collected include Cades Cove, Rich Mountain, Laurel Falls Trail, Mt. Le Conte (north slope), and Indian Creek.

A closely related species, *Sarcodon murrillii,* also grows in the Park. It has shorter teeth which when dry are very easily removed.

Figure 36f, about three-fourths natural size

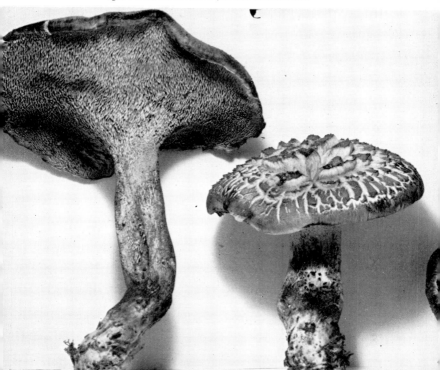

37

Stinkhorns

These strange fungus plants consist of a stalk, and either a cap or a head. In all of them there is at first an "egg" which breaks at the top and, by elongation of the stalk, the head is carried up. This elongation process takes place within two to four hours. At maturity they have a strong carrion-like odor—whence the common name stinkhorn.

The spores are borne at the tip imbedded in a sticky substance which attracts insects. The insect feeds on the sticky substance, and the spores, unharmed in the insect body, are finally deposited at a distance from the parent fungus.

Three species of stinkhorns have been found in the Park. Two of these, together with one species not yet found in the Park, are included in the key.

Key to the Stinkhorns

1. Fruiting body with a slender conic, or pointed, red head . . . . 37a, *Mutinus ravenelii*
1. Fruiting body not as above 2
  2. Cap, or head, a red net . . . .
  . . . . 37b, *Simblum sphaerocephalum*
  2. Cap, or head, dark, slimy, the extreme tip white . . .
  . . . . 37c, *Phallus ravenelii*

Figure 37a, about natural size

37a   *Mutinus ravenelii*

RAVENEL MUTINUS   UNPALATABLE

Fruiting body 2 to 4 inches high, upper portion pointed and bright red. Odor offensive. Stalk soft, spongy, pink, with white remnants of the volva at the base.

This attractive but foul-smelling stinkhorn has been found in Cades Cove, on soil, along a mixed woods, in June.

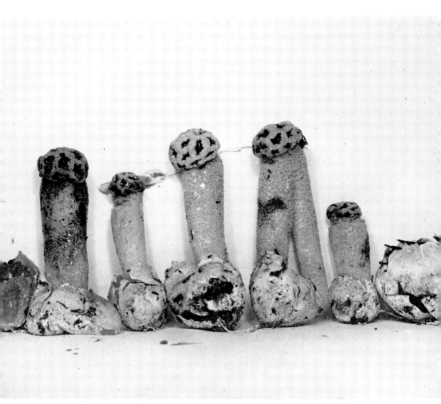

Figure 37b, about three-fourths natural size

37b   *Simblum sphaerocephalum*

ROUND-HEADED STINKHORN   UNPALATABLE

The entire fruiting body is 1½ to 2½ inches high, the head appearing as a round, thick, red net. Odor very offensive. The stalk is soft and spongy, pallid and narrowed somewhat at the base. The outer remains of the "egg" form a volva at the base.

Although this stinkhorn has not yet been found in the Park, it should occur there. It grows on grassy soil, and has been found near Knoxville, from May through November.

No one would think of eating this one.

37c *Phallus ravenelii*

Fruiting body at first an "egg," but developing rapidly to form a stalk, the lower end with a volva and the upper end bearing a head. Head ¾ to 1½ inches broad, perforated at the disk, olive-gray. Veil white, membranous, not extending below the cap. Stalk 2 to 4 inches long, pale-yellowish, fading to whitish, spongelike, with well-developed, white rhizomorphs at the base. Volva cuplike, membranous, whitish.

This stinkhorn is normally found on old sawdust piles where it often produces dozens of "eggs" which quickly develop the full-grown fruiting body. However, it was collected on rich soil, along a mixed woods, in Cades Cove, in June.

Its strong odor rules it out as an esculent.

Figure 37c, about two-thirds natural size

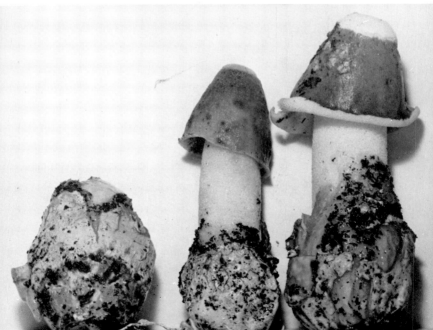

*Figures 38a, above and at right, about
natural size*

38

Calostoma

In this group, the fungus is at first a more or less
spherical body beneath the soil. The spongy stalk
elongates carrying the spore-bearing head into the air.
The head is more or less globose, with a mouth.

There are three species in the Park, two of which
are included here.

Key to the Calostomas

1. Cap (spore-sac) with a collar about its base . . . .
. . . . .38a, *Calostoma lutescens*
1. Cap without a collar . . . . .38b, *Calostoma ravenelii*

38a   *Calostoma lutescens*

YELLOW CALOSTOMA

At maturity, the fruiting body consists of a spongy, yellowish stalk, 2 to 3 inches high, bearing a globose head. The head is yellowish, with a red mouth. At its base is a collar.

This species differs from C. *cinnabarinus*, in which the head is red and without a collar at the base of the head, and C. *ravenelii* in which the head is clay to straw-colored and also lacks a collar at the base of the head.

Each year this curiosity is brought for identification by students and other interested persons. It seems to grow throughout the Park, especially at lower and middle elevations. Stations include: Greenbrier, road to Cherokee Orchard, the Sinks, and Cades Cove, June through January.

38b *Calostoma ravenelii*

The fruiting body is not gelatinous, and exhibits a spongy stalk bearing a rounded, yellowish head with a red mouth. Stalk ¾ to 2 inches high.

One may run across this species at almost any time of the year. Summer is its favorite growing season. Collections have been made in Cades Cove, in August and December; Brushy Mountain, in February; Mt. Sterling, in August; and at Elkmont, in March.

Figure 38b, about natural size

Pisolithus tinctorius is the only species of this genus known to be found in the Park.

39

Pisolithus

In the Park, one species of this genus is known. It is peculiar in its structure, and, growing half-buried, it doubtless is often overlooked. Its head is really a compound of several bodies which compose the fruiting structure. The skin of the fruiting body bears a pigment which stains cloth and paper—whence the species name *tinctorius*.

Figure 39a, section showing spore chambers, about natural size

39a   *Pisolithus tinctorius*

CHAMBERED PUFFBALL   EDIBILITY UNKNOWN

Fruiting body 2 to 5 inches broad, globose to pear-shaped, dull olive then brown to black, often tapering below to a stalklike base. Inner portion brownish or blackish, often with a metallic luster, at first showing (when cut) the spore-chambers, finally with brownish spore-powder. There is no mouth; the spores escape with the disintegrating of the fruiting body wall.

This peculiar fungus is scarcely a true puffball. When mature, if sudden pressure is applied, the spores do not puff out as in the puffballs. It is, however, a close relative.

Although it is commonly met in the early autumn around Knoxville, it has been found only in Cades Cove, in the Park, in pine woods, in August. More diligent search will doubtless reveal it at other collecting grounds in the Park. It grows in soil, usually about half-buried.

40

Cordyceps (Club-Heads)

Among the fascinating larger fungi of the Park are the club-heads, or species of *Cordyceps*. They live as parasites on either insect bodies or on other fungi.

The fruiting body consists of an erect stalk which bears the spores in tiny sunken chambers. The spore-bearing area develops toward the apex which may be more or less cylindric, club-shaped, or somewhat globose. Color of stalk varies, according to species, from flesh-colored to bright orange, brown, or black.

The club-heads grow from the buried bodies of dead insects, including grubs, ants, beetles, spiders, flies, cicadas, wasps, moths, butterflies, and caterpillars; or they may develop from fungi, especially species of *Elaphomyces* (relatives of truffles). None of the *Cordyceps* would appeal to the mycophagist.

Since seventeen species have been found in the Park, it is evident that this area is favorable for this group. Four are included here.

Key to the Cordyceps

1. Fruiting body with distinct, rather globose head; parasitic on false truffles ....*40a, Cordyceps capitata*
1. Not as above 2
    2. Cap bright orange; stalk white; parasitic on insect-pupae ....*40b, Cordyceps militaris*
    2. Cap and stalk dark-colored (grayish, olive, brown, or black) 3
3. Club-shaped stalks growing on false truffles ....
....................*40c, Cordyceps ophioglossoides*
3. Slender, more or less cylindric stalks growing on buried beetle larvae ....*40d, Cordyceps superficialis*

40a *Cordyceps capitata*

ROUND-HEADED CORDYCEPS   UNPALATABLE

Fruiting body 2 to 3½ inches high. Cap globose to egg-shaped, reddish-brown or blackish. Stalk olive-colored to yellowish.

This *Cordyceps* is parasitic on *Elaphomyces*, a relative of truffles. At times two or more stalks grow from the same host. It has been found at Indian Creek, near the Park Headquarters, and at Elkmont, in July and August. It was also found in January, near Elkmont.

Figure 40a, about natural size

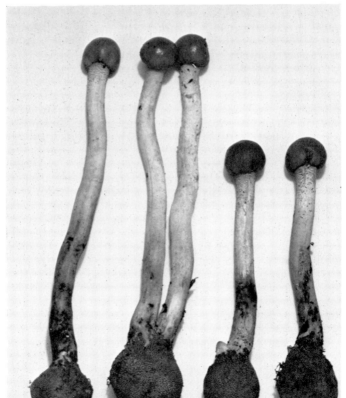

Figure 40b, about twice natural size

40b *Cordyceps militaris*

ORANGE-COLORED CORDYCEPS   UNPALATABLE

Fruiting body 1 to 2 inches high, bright orange, club-shaped. Stalk whitish, arising from the body of a more or less buried pupa of butterfly.

This bright-colored *Cordyceps* has been seen at several stations in the Park: on Clingmans Dome, Mt. Le Conte, Bote Mountain, Indian Creek, and along Roaring Fork. Once it was found on a rotting log, in which the pupa was buried. All collections thus far have been made during July, August, and September.

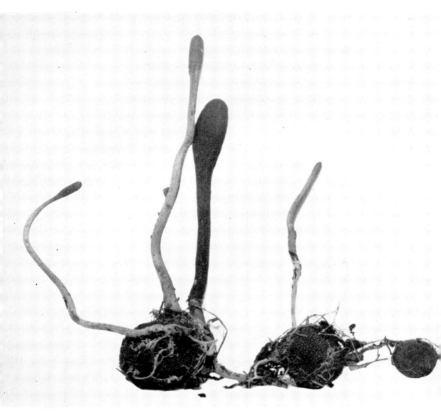

Figure 40c, about natural size

40c   *Cordyceps ophioglossoides*

UNPALATABLE

Fruiting body erect, club-shaped, 2 to 3 inches high. Head dark brown. Stalk olivaceous to blackish, the base with numerous fibers or strands extending into the fungus-host and on into the soil.

This species seems to be the most common of the *Cordyceps* group in the Park. It is parasitic on *Elaphomyces*, a relative of the truffles. It has been collected in July and August at Smokemont, Newfound Gap, Mt. Le Conte, Elkmont, and Cades Cove.

Figure 40d, slightly larger than natural size

40d   *Cordyceps superficialis*

SUPERFICIAL CORDYCEPS   UNPALATABLE

Fruiting body erect, slender throughout, 1 to 2½ inches high. Head not sharply distinct from the stalk, blackish, with black pimple-bodies. Stalk grayish-brown, slender.

This is one of the more rare species of *Cordyceps* in the Park. It has been found at Fighting Creek Gap (near Elkmont), on a beetle larva, in August. It appeared in a pine woods, during several successive summers at Highlands, North Carolina (outside the Park).

Helvella crispa is one of the five species of false morels found in the Great Smoky Mountains National Park.

41

Morels (True and False Morels)

The fruiting body of morels thus far found in the Park consists of a cap and stalk. The cap of true morels is provided with ribs and depressions, and so far as known all are edible. The cap of false morels takes the form of a brain (convoluted), or of a saddle, and at least some of these are poisonous! The species of false morels are not always identified with certainty; therefore, none of them should be eaten.

All morels (also called hickory-chickens or land-fish) are fleshy; otherwise, they are only remotely related to the mushrooms. In the Park, five species of true morels and five species of false morels have been found—ten in all—of which five are included in the key.

Key to the True and False Morels

1. Cap definitely ridged and fluted, with ribs and depressions (TRUE MORELS) 2
1. Cap saddle-shaped or convoluted like a brain (FALSE MORELS) 4
    2. Cap more or less globose to somewhat ovoid, not strikingly conic; ribs irregularly disposed; stalk not ribbed ....41a, Morchella esculenta
    2. Cap elongate or ovoid-elongate, conic, ribs extending more or less lengthwise; stalk somewhat ribbed at the base 3
3. Ribs of the cap darker than the interior of the pits ....
.....................41b, Morchella angusticeps
3. Ribs of the cap lighter in color than the interior of the pits; cap definitely conic, slender ....
..........................41c, Morchella conica
    4. Cap convoluted like a brain, brown; stalk 2 to 3 inches broad ....41d, Helvella caroliniana
    4. Cap more or less saddle-shaped, whitish to yellowish; stalk 1 inch or less in diameter, ribs rather sharp ....41e, Helvella crispa

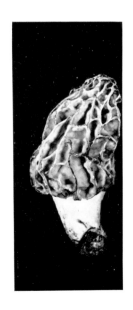

41a   *Morchella esculenta*

COMMON MOREL   EDIBLE

Cap, or head, elongated or nearly globose, with deep pits and ridges or ribs, about 1½ to 3 inches long and about 1 to 2 inches in diameter, gray-brown to yellowish-brown. Stalk 1½ to 2 inches long, whitish or yellowish.

This common, edible morel grows chiefly under apple trees and in deciduous woods. Although it may grow in coniferous woods, it has not yet been so reported. It has been found in Greenbrier, above Gatlinburg (Whittle's Place, near the Cherokee Orchard), and on Rich Mountain, in March and April.

Figures 41a, below and at left, about natural size
(photographs courtesy of W. R. Fisher)

41b *Morchella angusticeps*

Cap 1½ to 2½ inches long, 1 to 1½ inches broad, tip more or less conic, at times rather acute, pits elongated, ribs extending more or less lengthwise, and becoming smoky to black. Stalk 2 to 4½ inches long, paler than the cap.

The narrow-headed morel has been found under apple trees in Greenbrier, and at Whittle's Place near Cherokee Orchard, in March and April. Outside the Park, it grows abundantly in oak-hickory woods.

Figure 41b, about three-fourths natural size

41c   *Morchella conica*

CONIC MOREL   EDIBLE

Cap 2 to 3 inches long, 1 to 1½ inches broad, pits elongated, grayish-brown to yellowish-brown, ribs extending more or less vertically. Stalk 1½ to 2½ inches long, pallid, paler than the cap.

The conic morel is similar to the common morel, differing in its more slender, elongated, conic cap. It has been found in March and April, in Greenbrier and on Rich Mountain.

Figure 41c, about natural size

41d *Helvella caroliniana*

CAROLINA FALSE MOREL   EDIBILITY UNCERTAIN

Cap 2 to 5 inches high, diameter about the same as height or less, subglobose to ellipsoid, irregularly convoluted, dark brown. Stalk 3½ to 6 inches long, base 2 to 3 inches broad, whitish, tapering upward, with longitudinal, coarse ridges.

To date the Carolina false morel has not been found in the Park. It is large and conspicuous, and may be discovered in any future March or April. It may be looked for on soil in oak or other deciduous woods.

This false morel should not be eaten, since it may be confused with other species.

Figure 41e, about natural size

41e *Helvella crispa*

SADDLE-BACK FALSE MOREL   EDIBLE

Cap ⅓ to 1½ inches high, ½ to 1½ inches broad, saddle-shaped, margin often upturned, whitish at first, becoming yellowish in age, even or slightly convoluted. Stalk ½ to 2½ inches long, ribbed lengthwise of the stalk, colored much like the cap, hollow.

There are said to be color varieties, in which the cap may be flesh-colored, yellowish, or tan. The flavor is said to be good. The plants are small and normally are not abundant; consequently the saddle-back is not popular among mycophagists.

In the Park, it has been found in Cades Cove, in deciduous woods, in September, and at Elkmont, under hemlock, in August.

42

Coral Fungi (Clavaria and Similar Fungi)

In this group are included *Clavaria, Sparassis, Thelephora,* and *Tremellodendron.* For the most part these have a general resemblance, one to another.

They are fleshy to leathery, erect, and vary from simple club-shaped to repeatedly branched fruiting bodies.

In the Park, the coral fungi are represented by numbers of species, as follows: *Clavaria* 38, *Sparassis* 2, *Thelephora* 9, and *Tremellodendron* 5. In the key, six species are included.

Key to the Coral Fungi

1. Fruiting body unbranched, brownish to clay-colored. .
. . . . *42a, Clavaria pistillaris*
1. Fruiting body branched 2
   2. Branches rounded 3
   2. Branches flattened 5
3. Branches rather leathery, brownish with pale tips; odor offensive . . . . *42b, Thelephora palmata*
3. Branches fleshy 4
   4. Branches repeated and numerous, yellowish to buff, tips pink or red . . . . *42c, Clavaria botrytis*
   4. Branches yellow to brownish, few . . . .
   . . . . *42d, Clavaria muscoides*
5. Fruiting body a round mass of flat branches, resembling a lettuce head . . . . *42e, Sparassis crispa*
5. Fruiting body erect, with crowded branches . . . .
. . . . *42f, Tremellodendron pallidum*

Figure 42a, about three-fourths natural size

42a *Clavaria pistillaris*

PESTLE-SHAPED CLAVARIA   EDIBLE

The fruiting body varies from 1 to 5 inches high, and is an erect, club-shaped stalk. It is brown, tawny, to clay-colored, the tip rounded or blunt. The flesh is whitish, tender and soft, collapsing in age so that the stalk may be hollow at maturity or in age.

It is said to be of good flavor—any bitterness which may be present disappears on cooking.

This interesting *Clavaria* grows generally over the Park, in the woods, at both lower and higher elevations. Specimens in the Herbarium at The University of Tennessee are from Cataloochee and Thomas Ridge, in August, and were growing in mixed woods.

42b *Thelephora palmata*

The fruiting body is leathery-soft, brownish or brownish-purple, erect, much branched, the branches somewhat flattened, the tips whitish. Odor offensive. Stalk short, branching near the base, brownish.

This palm-leaf *Thelephora* has been found in July and August, at Elkmont and on the north slope of Mt. Le Conte, in mixed and coniferous woods.

Figure 42b, about natural size

42c *Clavaria botrytis*

Branched head 3 to 5 inches broad, branching and re-branching, the branches crowded, whitish, to cream or pinkish-buff, the tips blunt and reddish when young. Flesh brittle, mild and pleasant, rarely slightly bitter, odor slight. Stalk 1 to 2 inches long.

The shape of the head suggests a cluster of grapes, and is thus called *botrytis*. It is found on soil, in hemlock and mixed woods, at several stations scattered over the Park: Cades Cove, Rich Mountain, Elkmont, and Indian Creek, in June, July, August, and September.

It is said that for eating it must be well cooked.

Figure 42c, about two-thirds natural size

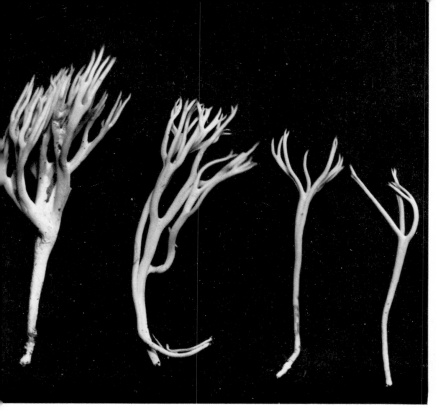

Figure 42d, about natural size

42d *Clavaria muscoides*

FORKED OR MOSS-CLAVARIA   EDIBLE

The whole plant from 1½ to 3 inches tall, with a distinct stalk and few to several branches, angles of the branches open, color yellowish to brownish. Flesh brittle, taste strong and like new meal, then bitter. Stalk about 1 to 1½ inches long.

This species represents one of the several forms displayed by *Clavaria*. It is supposedly rare in the South, but has been found growing in rich soil in deciduous and mixed woods, from June through August, at Indian Creek, at the Park Headquarters, and on the north slope of Mt. Le Conte, at 3000 feet.

Although it is moderately tough, it is reportedly edible.

42e *Sparassis crispa*

The fruiting body, varying from 4 to 6 inches in diameter, is a round mass or rosette of whitish, fused branches. The branches are more or less flat and leaflike, the mass suggesting the shape of a lettuce head. A short stalk is found at the base.

This is a rare and interesting find. It has been collected in Cades Cove only, in June, July, and August, in deciduous woods. It is said to be of excellent flavor.

In the Park there is another species, *Sparassis spathulata*, which differs from *S. crispa* in its broader, more leaflike, and less crowded branches, and a longer stalk.

42f *Tremellodendron pallidum*

The fruiting body consists of a short stalk and a head of tough branches. The whitish branches are flattened, and their tips, which tend to be dilated, extend upward to a common level, so that the head is more or less flat. The stalks are usually fused into a large mass, so that the body may be 2 to 5 inches broad, and at times nearly as high as broad.

The plant body is so leathery-tough that it would not be sought for eating. The name *Tremellodendron* means gelatinous tree.

This species grows commonly in and out of the Park, but being common there are no Park collections in The University of Tennessee Herbarium. It may be expected in deciduous woods in June, July, and August. There are four other related species in the Park.

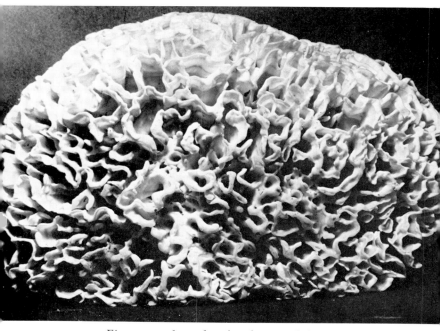

Figure 42e, about three-fourths natural size

Figure 42f, about three-fourths natural size

43

Xylaria (Dead-Man's-Fingers)

As the name *Xylaria* suggests, these fungi are wood-loving. Their dark brown or black, erect bodies extend into the air—whence the common designation dead-man's-fingers. They are distant relatives of earth-tongues and *Cordyceps* species.

There are eight species known in the Park, of which two of the more common kinds are included here. A key to species seems unnecessary.

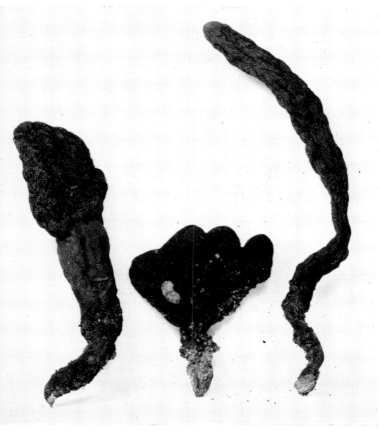

Figure 43a, about three-fourths natural size

43a *Xylaria polymorpha*

MANY-FORM XYLARIA   UNPALATABLE

Fruiting body erect, 2 to 6 inches high, dingy brown or black, variable in shape: club-shaped, fan-shaped and flat, at times lobed, occasionally nearly globose. Flesh pallid. Stalk short, often thick. Spores brown.

Being rather common in the Park, this species has been collected there only three times: at Indian Creek, on Mt. Le Conte, and Greenbrier, in August and September. It grows on or about decaying wood and logs.

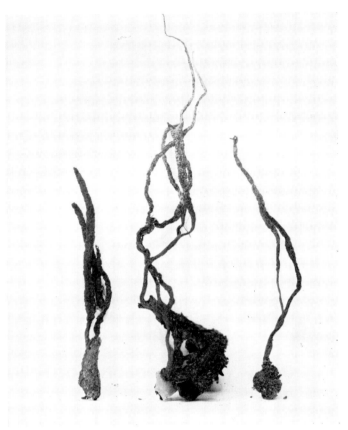

Figure 43b, about three-fourths natural size

43b *Xylaria hypoxylon*

WOOD-LOVING XYLARIA   UNPALATABLE

Fruiting body black, erect, 2½ to 6 inches high, slender, tapering at the tip, at times branched. Flesh pallid. Stalk short. Spores black.

This slender *Xylaria* grows on logs and rotting wood (at times buried wood) of both deciduous and coniferous trees. It has been found along Roaring Fork, at Elkmont, Indian Camp Creek, and Cataloochee, from June through September.

44

Earthtongues

The near relatives of the earthtongues are the morels. In general appearance, some of them at least resemble the simple, unbranched coral fungi, and the Xylarias. Others have a rather well-defined cap. All species are more or less fleshy. They grow on soil, humus and moss-covered logs, and may be found in dense coniferous and mixed woods. A very few species are found on humus submerged in shallow water, or on embankments where water drips continuously. Information relative to the edibility of earthtongues is indeed limited. Because of their small size, they are of little importance among edible species.

To date, thirty species have been found in the Park of which three are included in the key.

Key to the Earthtongues

1. Fruiting body black, clavate, viscid or slimy . . . .
. . . .*44a, Gloeoglossum difforme*
1. Fruiting body some shade of yellow 2
  2. Fruiting body clavate with a more or less distinct, somewhat flattened head . *44b, Microglossum rufum*
  2. Fruiting body variable: clavate, spathulate, irregularly and slightly branched . .*44c, Mitrula irregularis*

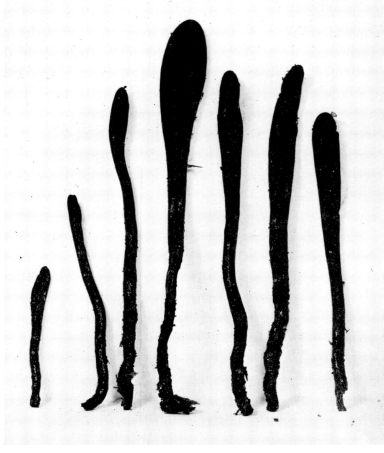

Figure 44a, about natural size

44a *Gloeoglossum difforme*

BLACK VISCID EARTHTONGUE   EDIBILITY UNCERTAIN

Fruiting body an erect, club-shaped, compressed stalk, 1½ to 5 inches high, black, viscid, at times shining to slimy-viscid. The brown spores are borne over the upper portion of the body.

Whether this earthtongue is edible or poisonous is uncertain. One of its close relatives, G. *glutinosum*, is said to be delicious when stewed.

A search of moss-covered logs in summer in dense woods should reveal this species. It has been collected in such a habitat in Cades Cove, in August.

44b *Microglossum rufum*

SMALL REDDISH EARTHTONGUE   EDIBILITY UNKNOWN

Fruiting body showing a fairly distinct head and stalk —the whole body 1 to 2½ inches high, clear yellow to orange-yellow. The head ovoid or compressed and wider than the slightly scaly stalk.

The reddish earthtongue has been found on soil, on humus, and on moss-covered logs in dense woods. Stations where it has been collected include Cades Cove, Mt. Le Conte, Greenbrier, and Indian Creek, from June through August.

Figure 44b, about natural size

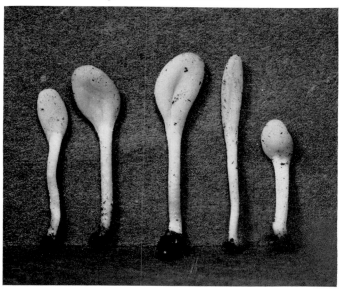

44c   *Mitrula irregularis*

Fruiting body variously shaped: cylindric, clavate, spathulate, at times slightly branched, always with a rather distinct stalk—the whole body ¾ to 2 inches high, pale orange-yellow. Stalk whitish, often tapering below.

One may not have to climb Mt. Le Conte or Clingmans Dome to find this earthtongue; but it is more certain to be found there than elsewhere. It develops annually along the trail about half-way from Forney Ridge Parking Area to the observation tower on Clingmans Dome, in September. Elsewhere it has been found on Mt. Le Conte, in September; near the Park Headquarters, in November; in Cades Cove, in November. It usually grows near moss, under fir or pine.

Figure 44c, about natural size

*Young plants are just opening in this picture of
Cyathus lesueurii.*

45

Bird's-Nest Fungi

These are so called because the fruiting body is
cup-shaped and contains a few rounded to lens-shaped
bodies. The whole picture suggests a bird's nest with
eggs.

A single plant begins as a closed globose or
slightly elongated body. Finally, opening, it exposes
the "eggs" within which are contained the spores.

They grow on soil, manure, or even decaying
wood. One species, *Cyathus lesueurii*, is included here.

45a *Cyathus lesueurii*

Fruiting body ¼ to ¾ inches high, goblet-shaped or vaselike, grayish above, brownish below, outer surface fibrous to felted, mouth surrounded by hairs; containing several egglike, blackish spore-cases.

Although two species of bird's-nest fungi have been found in the Park, the one described above has not yet been seen there.

The size and shape of this fungus would hardly suggest palatability.

Figure 45a, about natural size

This is the cup-shaped fruiting body of
Paxina acetabulum.

46

Cup Fungi

Within the Park there are many cup-shaped fungi.
Some are small, others up to 3 inches broad. Some
have a stalk; others lack this structure.

The cup fungi, also popularly called fairy-baths,
are rather closely related to the morels and to the earthtongues.

Many grow on soil, others on dung of various animals, decaying leaves, logs, and fallen limbs. At
times, they are found on trunks of dead trees. One has
only to look on the trunks and limbs of fir on Clingmans Dome or atop Mt. Le Conte, from May to
November, to see an abundance of the pale yellowish-
orange cup fungus, *Phialea crocea.*

In the Park, there are at present ninety-nine species of cup fungi on the list, of which two are included
here. A key hardly seems necessary.

Figure 46a, about two-thirds natural size

46a   *Paxina acetabulum*

CUP FUNGUS   EDIBLE

Cup 1 to 2 inches broad, about 1 inch deep, finally expanding and shallow, brown or blackish, externally ribbed and grayish-brown. Stalk ½ to 1½ inches long, pallid, ribbed, the ribs of the cup extending down the stalk.

This is one of approximately one hundred kinds of cup fungi in the Park, some of which are more spectacularly colored than this cup fungus.

One may expect to find this species near Indian Gap, under spruce, in July. It has been seen there more than once. It probably grows elsewhere on soil, in coniferous woods.

46b *Urnula craterium*

Cup ½ to 2½ inches broad when fully opened, margin of the cup notched and folded, externally carbon black or dark brown, hairy, rather tough and leathery. The interior of the cup is brownish-black, usually a bit paler than the outside. Stalk 1 to 2½ inches long, dark, often 2 to 4 stalks and cups bound together at the base.

It seems that I have collected this species near the Park without a single specimen from within the Park itself. It is most certainly there! It grows conspicuously on logs and fallen, decaying limbs, from March through May.

Flesh is limited and not attractive to the mycophagist.

Figure 46b, about three-fourths natural size

47

Earthstars

The earthstars are well-named. During development, an outer wall around the central spore-container
splits into a number of segments, or rays. Viewed
from above, they have the appearance of a star, and,
since they grow on the ground, they are called earthstars.

The earthstars are closely related to the puffballs,
bird's-nest fungi, and, a bit more remotely, to the stinkhorns and false truffles. These relatives, with the excep-
tion of *Scleroderma geaster*, do not show the distinctly
starlike rays at maturity found in the earthstars.

Within the Park, four species of earthstars have
been found. The one species treated here has not been
discovered actually growing in the Park.

47a *Geastrum morganii*

MORGAN'S EARTHSTAR   EDIBLE WHEN YOUNG

Fruiting body ¾ to 1½ inches broad, at first ovoid or bulb-shaped, wood-brown with a wine tint, the outer layer splitting to form triangular rays which surround the central, spore-bearing sac, and the spore-sac with an opening.

One should look for this fungus on soil near stumps and sawdust, from August to December. So far, it has not been found in the Park.

Figures 47a, left and below, about three-fourths natural size

48

Puff balls

These fungi are called puffballs because when pressure is applied suddenly the dry spores puff out in a cloud. In some species, the spores are released through an opening at the top; in others, they are released only by the breaking or disintegrating of the wall of the fruiting body.

They may ordinarily be seen at first as small spherical bodies. They soon reach full size, at which time their inner flesh is white and rather soft. In this stage they are good to eat. Later in development the inner flesh is transformed into a mass of spores.

The puffballs are near relatives of the earthstars, and more distant relatives of the bird's-nest fungi, the stinkhorns, and the false truffles.

Within the Park twenty species are now known, of which only one is included here. No key seems necessary.

Figure 48a, about natural size

48a *Lycoperdon perlatum*

DEVIL'S SNUFF-BOX   EDIBLE, WHEN YOUNG

Fruiting body top-shaped, 2 to 3½ inches tall, with a stalklike base, whitish when young, becoming grayish-brown, upper portion with mealy particles (spines) which fall away leaving small, round areas; at maturity there is an opening at the top. Flesh of head white and soft when young, becoming yellowish then olive with a mass of powder (the spores).

From May through November, or even later, one may find this common puffball in the Park. It has been found in Cades Cove, Tremont, Meigs Creek, Roaring Fork, on the north slope of Mt. Le Conte, and at the Chimneys. It grows on humus (leaves, decaying wood).

Glossary

ACRID (of the taste of a fruiting body or any of its parts), biting the tongue, peppery.

ADNATE (of the gills), broadly attached to the stalk.

ANASTOMOSE (of gills or ridges), interjoined or connected by ridges.

ANNULUS, see Ring.

APPRESSED (of scales, hairs), flattened down.

BULBOUS (of the stalk), enlarged at the base.

BUTTON, the young unexpanded cap.

CARTILAGINOUS (of the stalk), brittle, breaking with a snap.

CAESPITOSE, growing in tufts or clusters.

CAP, technically the pileus; the expanded portion of the mushroom which bears the gills on its lower surface.

CLAVATE (of the stalk), enlarged above or below, clublike.

DECIDUOUS, falling; deciduous woods are composed of trees which drop their leaves in the autumn.

DECURRENT (of the gills), extending down the stalk.

DELIQUESCE, a dissolving or liquefying by self-digestion (in species of *Coprinus*).

DISK (of the cap), central portion of the cap-surface.

EMARGINATE (of the gills), notched near the stalk.

FAIRY RING, a circle formed by a group of mushrooms or puffballs; the circle may widen from year to year.

FIBRILLOSE, said of a surface of the cap or stalk bearing hairs or threadlike structures.

FLESHY, of soft consistency; a fleshy mushroom soon decays; in contrast to tough, leathery, or woody.

FRUITING BODY, the spore-bearing structure. In a typical mushroom it is composed of the stalk, cap, and gills.

GELATINOUS, jelly-like; usually slimy or slippery.

GENUS, a term used in classification; a genus embraces one or more species. One or more genera make up a family; the first name in the Latin binomial; in the binomial *Amanita verna* the generic name is *Amanita*.

GILLS, bladelike structures on the lower side of the cap.

GLABROUS, lacking hairs, scales, or other surface decorations.

GLUTINOUS (of the cap or stalk), covered with a thick, jelly-like material.

HUMUS, the decaying organic matter mostly of plant origin, in the soil.

HYPHA, a threadlike fungal-filament.

INNER VEIL (Partial Veil), a sheath which, in the young mushroom, extends from the stalk to the cap-margin; it covers the young gills.

LATEX, a liquid (colorless or colored) present in *Lactarius* and a few others, observed when the fruiting body is injured.

MARGIN, the edge (said of the cap and gill).

MYCELIUM, a collective term for a group of fungal threads, or hyphae.

MYCORRHIZA, literally a fungus-root; an association of a fungus (often a mushroom) with the small roots of trees and some other plants.

OUTER VEIL (Universal Veil), a webby or membranous, at times jelly-like, sheath enclosing the young mushroom.

PARASITE, an organism living on and at the expense of another organism.

PARTIAL VEIL, see Inner Veil.

PILEUS, see Cap.

PORE, the mouth of a tube (in boletes and polypores).

POROID, having pores or porelike structures.

RHIZOMORPH, a cordlike strand composed of hyphae.

RING, a band encircling the stalk, usually near the apex, resulting from the breaking of the inner veil.

SCALES, applied to various types of structural decorations on the cap and stalk; scales may be remnants of the outer veil, or may be loosened portions of the surface.

SCLEROTIUM, a hard resting body.

SERRATE, a saw-tooth-like edge (of the gills).

SERRULATE, minutely serrate.

SHEATH, a covering.

SPECIES, a term used in classification; a group of individuals or varieties and forms make up a genus; the second name in a Latin binomial; in *Amanita verna* the species name is *verna*.

SPORE, a special reproductive body, usually one-celled.

SQUAMULE, a small scale.

STALK, the stem of mushrooms and some of their relatives.

STRIGOSE, having long, coarse, stiff hairs.

SUBSTRATUM, the substance on which a mushroom or other fungus grows.

TOMENTOSE, matted and woolly, usually of long, soft filaments.

UMBILICATE, a navel-like depression (of the cap).

UMBONATE (of the cap), conspicuously elevated on the central portion of the cap.

UNIVERSAL VEIL, the sheath, veil, or covering found in some mushrooms; it may be jelly-like, webby, or membranous. When present, its remnants are often found as scales on the cap or as a cup or as scales at the stalk-base.

VISCID, sticky especially when wet.

VOLVA, the remains of the outer veil after it breaks. The volva may show as a cup or as scales at the stalk-base, or as scalelike patches on the cap.

ZONATE (of the cap), with concentric bands of colors.

Some Books on Mushrooms
and Their Relatives

I. BOOKS CURRENTLY AVAILABLE

Christensen, Clyde M. *Common Fleshy Fungi.* 246 pp. 1955. Burgess Publishing Co., Minneapolis.

Christensen, Clyde M. *Common Edible Mushrooms.* 124 pp. 1959. Charles T. Bransford, Newton Center, Massachusetts.

Coker, W. C. and Alma H. Beers. *The Boletaceae of North Carolina.* 96 pp. 65 plates and frontispiece. 1943. The University of North Carolina Press, Chapel Hill.

Coker, W. C. and Alma H. Beers. *The Stipitate Hydnums of the Eastern United States.* 211 pp. 60 plates. 1951. The University of North Carolina Press, Chapel Hill.

Pilát, A. *A Handbook of Mushrooms.* 90 pp. 94 colored plates. Spring Books, London. (A translation from the Czechoslovakian language by Helen Watney-Kaczerova.)

Ramsbottom, John. *Mushrooms and Toadstools.* 306 pp. 84 color and 58 black and white figures. 1953. Macmillan Co., New York.

Smith, Alexander H. *Puffballs and Their Allies in Michigan.* 131 pp. 43 plates. 1951. University of Michigan Press, Ann Arbor.

Smith, Alexander H. *The Mushroom Hunter's Field Guide.* 197 pp. 155 photographs. 1958. University of Michigan Press, Ann Arbor.

Thomas, W. S. *Field Book of Common Mushrooms.* 369 pp. Illustrated. 1948. G. P. Putnam's Sons, New York.

II. BOOKS NOW LISTED AS OUT-OF-PRINT

Atkinson, George F. *Mushrooms: Edible, Poisonous, etc.* 275 pp. 223 figures. 1900. Andrus and Church, Ithaca, New York.

Gibson, W. H. *Our Edible Toadstools and Mushrooms.* 337 pp. 30 colored plates, 57 figures. 1895. Harper and Bros., New York.

Güssow, H. T. and W. S. Odell. *Mushrooms and Toadstools. An account of the common edible and poisonous fungi of Canada.* 274 pp. 128 plates. 1927. Dominion Experiment Farms, Ottawa, Canada.

Hard, M. E. *The Mushroom, Edible and Otherwise.* 609 pp. 66 plates. 505 figures. 1908. Ohio Library Co., Columbus.

Kauffman, C. H. *The Agaricaceae of Michigan.* 2 vols. 924 pp. 172 plates. 1918. Lansing.

Krieger, Louis C. C. *The Mushroom Handbook.* 512 pp. 126 figures and 32 color plates. 1936. Macmillan Co., New York.

Marshall, Nina L. *The Mushroom Book.* 173 pp. Numerous illustrations. 1923. Doubleday, Page and Co.

McIlvaine, Charles. *One Thousand American Fungi.* 729 pp. 181 plates. 1912. The Bowen-Merrill Co., Indianapolis.

Pomerleau, Rene. *Mushrooms of Eastern Canada and the United States.* 302 pp. Illustrated. 1951. Montreal, Canada.

Ramsbottom, John. *Poisonous Fungi.* 32 pp. 16 color plates. 1945. The King Penguin Books, London and New York.

Ramsbottom, John. *Edible Fungi.* 45 pp. 24 color plates. Revised edition. 1948. The King Penguin Books, London and New York.

Rolfe, R. T. and F. W. Rolfe. *The Romance of the Fungus World.* 309 pp. 85 figures. 1926. J. B. Lippincott Co., Philadelphia.

Smith, Alexander H. *Common Edible and Poisonous Mushrooms of Southeastern Michigan.* 71 pp. 15 plates. 1938. Cranbrook Institute of Science, Bloomfield Hills, Michigan.

Smith, Alexander H. *Mushrooms in Their Natural Habitats.* 626 pp. 231 stero-photographs. 2 vols. 1949. Sawyer's Inc., Portland, Oregon.

Swanton, E. W. *Fungi and How to Know Them. An Introduction to Field Mycology.* 210 pp. 48 plates. 1932. Methuen and Co., London.

Wakefield, Elsie M. and R. W. G. Dennis. *Common British Fungi.* 290 pp. 111 colored plates and 6 text figures. 1950. P. R. Gawthorn.

Index